"An entertainingly written and encouraging book on how to manage goats humanely and holistically. Both new and experienced 'goat folks' will find ideas and tools to improve their animals' lives in these pages."

Judith M. Shoemaker, DVM, internationally known
integrative veterinary care educator and practitioner

"What a little gem of a book Carrie has written. *The Energetic Goat* is a practical manual that introduces the reader to the new frontier of vibrational medicine and energy diagnosis. It outlines a step-by-step methodology that allows anyone to tap into 'the field,' the universal database of consciousness that holds the answers to all of our questions: The cosmic cloud, if you will, also known in quantum physical circles as the Zero Point Field, and in spiritual circles, for those who dare to go there, as Carrie does, as God-energy.

"Carrie has laced her book with humor and her own observations on natural health care for goats based on her years of experience in the field. I was delighted with this book. It's a valuable resource not only for goat owners who want to access answers but for anyone interested in connecting with the most incredible database ever known, the Universal Mind.

"Thank you, Carrie. Well done."

Donna M. Starita, DVibM, DVM

"Carrie has done a great job explaining both in print and in photo how to work with muscle testing and reflex assessment in goats to help determine their nutritional and health care needs. Her book gifts herd owners with these easy-to-use, wonderful aids for their tool belt in alternative wellness assessment, enabling the reader to have more control over the overall health of their herd."

Katherine A. Drovdahl, MH CR CA DipHIR CEIT QTP,
author of The Accessible Pet, Equine and Livestock Herbal
and CEO of Fir Meadow LLC

The Energetic Goat

The Energetic Goat

A Practical Guide to Applied Kinesiology,
Contact Reflex Analysis &
Dowsing for Your Herd's Health

Carrie Eastman

Acres U.S.A.
Austin, Texas

The Energetic Goat

Copyright © 2015, Carrie Eastman

Although the author and publisher have made every effort to ensure that the information in this book was correct at press time, the author and publisher do not assume and hereby disclaim any liability to any party for any loss, damage, or disruption caused by errors or omissions, whether such errors or omissions result from negligence, accident, or any other cause.

Acres U.S.A.
P.O. Box 301209
Austin, Texas 78703 U.S.A.
512-892-4400 • fax 512-892-4448
info@acresusa.com • *www.acresusa.com*

Printed in the United States of America

Front cover photography © Pawel Nowik/iStock/Thinkstock
Interior illustrations © S. F. Soeder 73, 76, 81

Library of Congress Cataloging-in-Publication Data

Eastman, Carrie, 1967– author.
    The energetic goat : a practical guide to applied kinesiology, contact reflex
        analysis & dowsing for your herd's health / Carrie Eastman. —
      opb edition.
      pages cm
    Includes index.
    ISBN 978-1-60173-124-1 (pbk.)
    ISBN 978-1-60173-125-8 (ebook)
    1. Goats—Health. 2. Goats—Diseases—Alternative treatment. 3. Reflexology
(Therapy) 4. Holistic veterinary medicine. 5. Kinesiology. 6. Dowsing. I. Title.

SF968.E32   2015   636.3'9—dc23

2015015639

To Daisy Mae, the little goat
that started it all

Table of Contents

Acknowledgments

There are so many people that helped this book come into being.

Thank you to my husband, Jim, for all your ideas and help. You supported and encouraged me from my days of "just having a couple goats to balance the pastures" to the expanded herd to finally "I'm going to write a book."

Thank you, Aunt Nadine. You were my first exposure to energy and body work as a toddler, and your influence shaped everything that followed.

A huge shout-out to my mom for keeping me on the holistic path as a child. And to my dad for his belief that I really could write a book. It just took me thirty years to find my topic. I trust Dad is smiling down on this.

And thank you to my heart dad, Carl, for his encouragement and support.

A big thanks to the many medical professionals and amazing healers and teachers who helped me and my animals and taught me so much. Dr. Charles Gagarin, Dr. Christopher Gouse, Dr. Regan Golob, Kelley Mills, Judy Sinner, Jim Zamzow, Dr. Patricia Whittaker, Dr. Ed Sheaffer, and Dr. Donna Starita. All of you mentored me and taught me so much along this path.

Thank you to my model, Amy Phelps, for your services and suggestions, and for plenty of laughter on a freezing photoshoot day.

Thank you to my fellow goat lover and illustrator extraordinaire Susan Falcon Soeder. Your willingness to indulge my nerdy side and talk anatomy, physiology, and chemistry as well as giggle and coo over adorable kids helped make this possible.

Thank you to Kat, Kristie, and Molly for your herbal wisdom and encouraging words.

Thank you to Cody and family, Denny, and Ken for all you do to keep Oak Hill running.

And my profoundest thanks to Acres U.S.A., especially Fred for giving an unknown author a chance and Amanda for your editing and willingness to walk me through the publishing process. Bless you.

Preface

From the time I could toddle, an honorary aunt and my mother both used reflex points, alternative therapies, and healthy diet to help me grow up strong and healthy. I thought everyone looked at health the way we did. We focused on maintaining health and trusted the body to heal itself, and we rarely reached for chemicals, drugs, or the care of regular doctors unless necessary. I was fortunate to have an old-school pediatrician who did just what was necessary and nothing more. Interestingly, as I got older and headed off to college I continued these approaches for myself but took care of my dogs and horses using conventional traditional Western medicine. It wasn't until my horse was diagnosed with ringbone, sidebone, navicular syndrome, and arthritis and recommended for retirement at age twelve that I connected the dots.

Shortly before his diagnosis, this horse had given me a nasty case of whiplash during a spook. I went searching for a chiropractor. That chiropractor knew a horseman and healer named Regan Golob and asked me to organize a seminar with Regan. That seminar changed all our lives. I finally made the connection and began applying the health principles I grew up with to my horses and dogs. A few years and many classes with Regan later, I wanted a couple goats to balance my pastures. Well, as anyone with goats can tell you, they are like potato chips. Start with a couple and end up with a herd. I began experimenting with applying everything I had learned about bodywork and nutrition for horses and people to the goats. I found that I could tailor my nutrition program better, my goats were healthier, and I was saving money knowing exactly what I needed to purchase and what I could skip. The herd is on its fifth generation now using these approaches. I have had no deaths due to acute illness. I have needed no chemical dewormers. The herd is thriving. My hope is that this book will offer you those same money-saving wellness options. And by the way, that horse that was scheduled to retire at twelve years old? He was sound by fourteen and lived to thirty.

Do I Sell Any of the Products Mentioned in this Book?

I am an independent distributor for several products mentioned in the book. You can find the full list and relevant links on the Resources page.

Some might ask if this is a conflict of interest. My answer is the same I was given by a mentor, friend, and fellow distributor. "If I find a product that works better and tests better than anything else I have seen, even better than something I could make or grow myself, how is sharing that a conflict of interest?"

I am always on the hunt for new and better ways to keep my goats healthy. Folks ask me to suggest products on a daily basis. If it's good enough, in fact the very best I can find, for my own goats, wouldn't it be pretty silly not to share that with others? And if I have spent hours researching and testing and asking questions, that has value. If I were a master herbalist offering health consultations and making my own herbal blends, is there a conflict of interest in consulting and selling my blends?

I am very careful to explain why a certain product tests better for my animals and teach people how to look for their own best answers, which may or may not be the same as mine. I tell people about and even endorse product lines that I have no financial stake in.

Finally, I am fine if someone chooses a product other than the one I sell. If it tests well for your goats, use it. My greatest desire is to see your goats thrive using whatever products work best for them and your situation.

Introduction:
Why Learn Muscle Testing, Reflex Points, and Dowsing?

There are several reasons to learn these techniques. First, it will save you money. I guarantee it. No more feeding supplements you don't need; no more feeding medications you don't need. Pick and choose what works best for each goat in each season, a particular age group, or your herd specifically. Using these techniques, you no longer have to throw everything including the kitchen sink at a goat or even the herd in the hope that something in there can solve your issue.

Ever had problems with the goats rejecting a particular product? You can muscle test right in the store to see if the product will do the job *and* agree with your goats.

Wondering if it's time to copper bolus again? Wondering which supplement to use? Wondering if that last batch of hay is a good one? All of these questions can be resolved using these techniques, just as farmers and healers have been doing for hundreds of years.

I'm New to Muscle Testing, Reflex Points, and Dowsing. Is This Book a Good Place to Start Learning?

Yes! Very much yes!

Not only do I give you step-by-step instruction on the basic techniques, including common variations, I also explain how to adapt other techniques to suit your personal preferences. There are pictures. There are diagrams. There are sample case histories for you to follow. I have also included a chart cross-referencing some popular product lines with common goat issues.

This Book is for Experienced Users, Too!

For readers who have years of experience with these testing techniques, you may find some new variations of testing techniques that you have not tried before. You will also find a copyrighted human reflex point chart to use for surrogate testing that has never appeared in print before. Finally, you will find a very useful product line and goat issue cross-reference chart in the back to speed up your testing.

Is This Information Only for Organic Holistic Herds Following Eastern Medicine Philosophies?

Nope. While many of us *are* Eastern-medicine oriented, and usually holistic, the testing techniques can be used for any feed, supplement, chemical, or medicine.

You will notice many chapters on holistic goat keeping in this book. There are lots of good published resources out there right now about Western medicine–standard, conventional, chemicals-allowed (how many labels can I find?) goat keeping. There are far fewer resources devoted to alternative, holistic, chemical-free goat keeping.

My personal philosophy is to use whatever product tests well for a given situation. Sometimes that will be an herb or supplement, sometimes a chemical or medicine. So be it. My goal is to encourage the greatest health of my goats. If a supplement or method tests well on that goat at that time, I trust the answer.

I would encourage readers to keep an open mind, look at the evidence behind the techniques, and explore how these tests can be used to improve your own herd, right now, with whatever philosophy you follow.

1

The Basics of Muscle Testing, Reflex Points, and Dowsing

I refer to applied kinesiology (muscle testing), contact reflex analysis (reflex points), and dowsing techniques collectively as energy testing. All are based on the same basic principles. Goat and human bodies are composed of protons, neutrons, and electrons, all of which make up atoms. These atoms have electrical properties, or to put it another way, protons have a positive charge, electrons have a negative charge, and neutrons are neutral. So we are all beings made up of energy, electrical energy.

Energy moves and travels and can be conducted over even great distances. Air, water, bodies—everything is made up of atoms. The vibration of one atom is thus transmitted to the one next to it, and so on and so on, covering great distances in a flash. A technique called Kirlian photography, or auric field photography, has actually documented the energy field that surrounds all living beings.

When doing muscle testing and dowsing, you are tapping into these fields to send and receive information about the body.

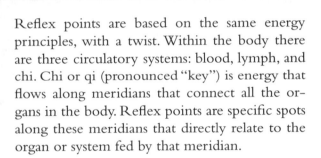

Reflex points are based on the same energy principles, with a twist. Within the body there are three circulatory systems: blood, lymph, and chi. Chi or qi (pronounced "key") is energy that flows along meridians that connect all the organs in the body. Reflex points are specific spots along these meridians that directly relate to the organ or system fed by that meridian.

Polarity, Hydration, and Other Complicating Factors

Polarity

You know how magnets have an end that repels and an end that attracts? Those are poles, sometimes called north and south. All animals and people have a north and south pole. The division between the poles is at the midline. If a person is standing, you are divided at your solar plexus. If a goat is standing on four hooves, the goat is divided at her midline, parallel to the ground. If you lie down, you are now divided at your midline. If you can get your goat to stand on her hind legs and dance, she is now divided at her solar plexus (and your dancing goat could become famous).

How to test for flipped polarity in a subject or surrogate.

Occasionally, your poles can flip, meaning north becomes south and south, north. In people, having a flipped polarity makes you feel "off." Your vision is slightly darker, life feels just a little bit down, your reflexes are a bit slower, and you may be a bit clumsy. Your energy testing work will be all over the place, and often animals will shy away from you or otherwise react in unusual ways. I would imagine that it feels similar for the animals. Flipped polarity will affect the energy flow in the body.

Poles can be flipped by traveling at speeds above thirty-five miles per hour, overhead power lines, exposure to strong electrical fields, getting shocked, fluorescent lighting, and anything metal that connects across a midline, either side to side or top to bottom. For example, in humans (I'm assuming your goat doesn't wear glasses) wire-rimmed glasses or underwire bras both connect across your midline and can flip your polarity.

There is a muscle test to check if polarity is flipped in people. The test requires two people. If both people have correct polarities, you can surrogate test the polarity of an animal. To test for flipped polarity:

1. The tester stands facing the testee.
2. The testee holds her right arm straight out to the side with the elbow locked and wrist limp so the hand dangles. This stance isolates the weaker shoulder muscles and makes the test easier.
3. The tester places her right hand on the testee's left shoulder.
4. The tester then places her left first and second fingers on the wrist of the testee's right arm.
5. The tester then tests to see if the testee's right arm holds strong on the command "Hold strong." The arm should remain strong.*
6. The tester then places the third or middle finger of her right hand on the testee's forehead between and just above the eyes (over the third eye).
7. Holding the finger in place, the tester again asks the testee to hold strong and tests the strength of the testee's right arm.
8. If the arm goes weak and drops, the testee has correct polarity.
9. If the arm stays strong the polarity is reversed and must be corrected.
10. Follow the instructions below for correcting polarity and retest.

If the polarity refuses to correct, see the following sections on hydration and electrolytes.

If polarity is just fine and you do the polarity correction anyway, no harm is done. Because testing for flipped polarity requires two people, and because we live in a world designed to flip polarity regularly, I find it is simpler just to assume polarity is flipped and clear myself and my goat before I start to test.

To clear polarity on yourself:
1. Hold the first and second finger of your right hand together, and curl your thumb and the rest of your fingers into your palm.
2. With those two fingers only, touch above your right eye.

---

* The arm "staying strong" means the arm locks firmly in place. This is not a contest of strength. Obviously, a larger, stronger man testing a petite woman can force her arm down. Strength means an instant firming/locking of the muscles. If the arm bobbles, weakens, or drops, all those reactions indicate a negative/no/weakened reaction.

3. Now stroke across your forehead from above your right eye to above your left eye once.
4. Lift your fingers away from your forehead.
5. Move your fingers back to above your right eye and stroke again.
6. Repeat for a total of three to five strokes.

To clear your goat:

Follow the same steps except start above your goat's right eye. If you are facing your goat, your goat's right eye will be on your left. Do not start above your goat's left eye.

Hydration

Start drinking. Have your goat join you for a drink.

Seriously, both goat and human bodies are composed of 50–75 percent water by weight. If you or your goats are dehydrated, electrical signals and energy are not going to move or transmit well. Check yourself and your goat by pinching a fold of skin. It should snap back into place. If it slowly returns to shape, or even worse, forms a tent and stays there, you are dehydrated and should go no further without rehydrating. For people, I like to use the skin on the back of the hand. For goats, I pinch skin on the side of the neck.

How to clear the polarity of a subject or surrogate.

Electrolytes and Mineral Balance

An electrolyte is any substance that contains free ions that conduct electricity. All mammals need electrolytes to function. Electrolytes include sodium (Na^+), potassium (K^+), calcium (Ca^{2+}), bicarbonate (HCO_3^-), magnesium (Mg^{2+}), chloride (Cl^-), hydrogen phosphate (HPO_4^{2-}), and hydrogen carbonate (HCO_3^-). Electrolytes come from foods high in these substances and from electrolyte supplements.

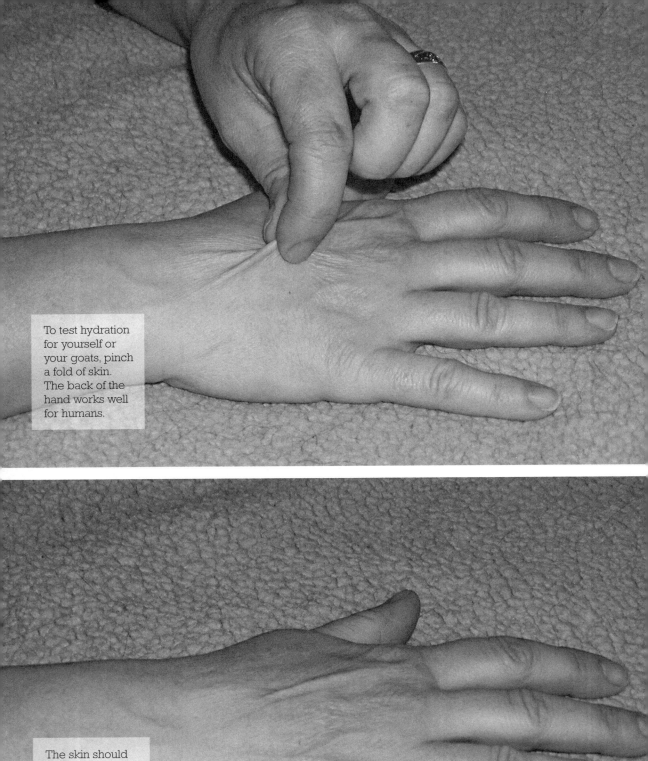

To test hydration
for yourself or
your goats, pinch
a fold of skin.
The back of the
hand works well
for humans.

The skin should
immediately
snap back into
place. The slower
it takes for the
skin to return to
normal, the more
dehydrated the
subject.

To test your goats for dehydration, pinch the skin on the side of its neck.

As the body needs electrolytes to conduct nerve impulses, move muscles, and circulate energy, energy testing will be affected if the body is low on electrolytes. If you find you are getting strange or inconsistent testing results, you may need to take some electrolytes, wait an hour, and try again.

Emotions

Strong emotions and preferences can influence the results of energy testing. Do your best to let go of any attachment to a particular answer or outcome. If you are dowsing, close your eyes while the pendulum starts to swing. If you are testing while holding a product, don't read the label. If you are dowsing from a list, cover up the list names. If you are unable to detach from an answer, ask someone else to perform the test for you. If you go into a situation believing that a certain answer is best, you will get that answer, whether it's the correct one or not. As a mentor of mine is fond of reminding me, "Would you rather be right, or be healthy?"

Doubt and trust are also factors. The more you work with these techniques, the more confident with them you will become. As your confidence grows, your accuracy and skill improve. Truly confident testers are able to work over great distances and test products they have never handled or worked with. Start with small steps. Work with products you have on hand so you can physically touch them. Choose tests that involve physical contact with your goat. If you get partway through a testing session and start getting inconsistent answers, your doubt will grow, and it may be best to step back and start over at a different time or with a different technique.

Trusting the answers is also important. You may sometimes get suggested remedies or dosages that are off-label. While you should always use common sense and consult a medical professional for unusual remedies, be aware that this can occur and often the answers are accurate and effective. My favorite example is toothpaste and sarcoids on horses. Someone muscle tested that fluoride toothpaste was the topical remedy for a sarcoid. After checking that there was no risk in using toothpaste in this very unconventional manner, the toothpaste was applied. The sarcoid fell off and never returned.

A final caution about strong opinions, directed just at the holistic Eastern medicine folks: There will be times that your testing will indicate a drug or chemical remedy. This becomes your personal choice whether to honor that answer. I personally feel that if the body is requesting a substance that I normally would avoid on principal, I will honor that choice. Especially during the transition phase from Western to Eastern health, animals will sometimes test for things like chemical wormers when their bodies are not yet healthy enough to handle the worms with herbal remedies.

Permission and the Greatest Good

I always ask permission before testing. I ask, "Is this test for the greatest good?" "Do I have permission to do this testing at this time?" If I get a "no," I respect that answer and come back another time. I personally like to say a little prayer also. Some folks ask for white light, some surround their work with a pink bubble, some pray for God's protection (or gods' or goddesses'). My point is simply put yourself in a place mentally and emotionally that feels safe and centered, calm and grounded, in whatever way works for you.

Overdoing It

Sometimes the goat may not be strong enough to tolerate a particular remedy or a detoxification process, or the goat's body may be busy with another higher healing priority. After getting a response to a dowsing question, I always ask "Can _____ (fill in the name) tolerate this _____ (fill in the name of the remedy or therapy) at this time?" If I get a "no," I will wait and ask about that same remedy or therapy at a later date. Because reflex points provide such a direct, clear, unbiased answer, I often skip this safety check when using reflex points. However, this question is critical for any testing technique other than reflex points. Do *not* skip this question.

2

The Many Ways to Muscle Test Goats

Energy testing can refer to muscle tests, reflex points, or dowsing. You can test alone or with a helper. You can test while in physical contact with the goat, by using a snip of hair from the goat, or, when you get truly confident, away from the goat, just holding the image of the goat in your mind. You can test using actual samples of the product you are testing or you can substitute other ways to represent the herb, remedy, oil, or other therapy. For example, some folks write the name of the remedy on a piece of paper and test with that. Some folks use the empty container the remedy was stored in. Some carry around testing kits containing pinches of each common remedy.

Product and Remedy Samples

In the beginning, when you are building your trust in the process, it is best to have the actual herb, homeopathic treatment, supplement, essential oil, or other remedy in hand. You will hold the remedy against the goat while performing the test. Remember, every remedy or product has its own energy signature or vibration because it is made up of atoms, just as you are. Keep in mind that the energy field or auric field extends out from both your body and the goat's body, and in fact the vibrations of that field transmit over very long distances. As you gain confidence and trust in the process, you will find that you no longer need to hold the sample against the goat. Just bringing the sample within both of your energy fields will be enough.

As you advance further, you will trust the long-distance vibrations that every sample or living being produces, and you will find that you can test successfully from greater and greater distances. You will also find as you advance that rather than using the actual sample, you can write the sample name on a piece of paper and test with that, or hold a vision of the sample in your mind.

I prefer to have handled a sample at least once to have that memory of its vibration available to me. Advanced practitioners are able to tap into the universal consciousness and work with samples they have never touched.

HINT

The small plastic, snap-lid containers used to hold fecal samples are the perfect size to hold a pinch of a remedy. You can fit an entire kit of these sample containers in a travel box. The following sections cover a wide selection of testing options, although this list is by no means comprehensive. An internet search is likely to reveal even more possible ways to test your goat.

Touch Your Goat

Yes, really. Touch your goat. Muscle testing depends on your energy field, called your etheric body or aura,* being in contact with the goat's energy field. In the beginning, this is easiest to do by making sure you are in physical contact with your goat. As you get more advanced, you will find that being close is enough, and the really advanced folks are able to work at great distances. Any part of your body can be in contact. For tests that use two hands, I just nudge my foot up against the goat's hoof or lean a leg against the goat's body. For one-handed tests, you can touch the goat with your other hand. For tests that use two people, the

---

* The etheric body, also called ether-body, aether body, vital body, or subtle body (as opposed to the physical body, but not the same as the astral body), is the connection between the physical body and the "higher" bodies.

person being tested should make contact with the goat, not the person doing the testing.

"My goat won't let me touch her." Well, did you offer flowers? Treats? Dinner and a movie? Still no luck? Your best bet in this case is to do two things. First, come up with a plan to work with your goat on becoming comfortable with being handled. The Tellington TTouch method is a combination of specific non-habitual touches, lifts, and body movements that awaken cellular intelligence and can reprogram fear, excitability, and other emotional issues. You can learn about using TTouch on their website, www.ttouch.com. Essential oils or flower essences are more options for changing emotions. Essential oils are concentrated oils distilled from plants and herbs. I suggest finding a trained practitioner to work with you, as essential oils are extremely powerful and can be misused. Bach flower essences are boiled or sun-steeped infusions of flowers in water. You can find more information on the Bach website, www.bachflower.com. Finally, the Emotional Freedom Technique (EFT), a psychological acupressure method recommended by Dr. Joseph Mercola, can be used to clear and reprogram emotions. All the free resources you need to get started with EFT are available on founder Gary Craig's website, www.emofree.com.

Second, practice your testing on someone until you're really confident, and then use the advanced technique of testing from a distance. Keep your intention that you are testing that particular goat firmly in your mind and heart, and then proceed with any of the testing processes described in this book. It works, even from across the country. Rather than get into detailed scientific explanations of how and why it works, I'll just say that cell phone signals can cross thousands of miles. All living beings are composed of protons, neutrons, electrons—we are all energy. I have had a vet on the opposite coast pinpoint the exact tooth that was damaged. 'Nuff said.

One-Person Tests

Interlocked Fingers

I'm going to assume you are right-handed. All you left-handed muscle testers, no discrimination intended. You can easily reverse the hands and get good results. So, for the right-handed.

The setup:
1. Touch your thumb and first finger of your left hand together at the tip to form a circle, like you are making the OK sign.

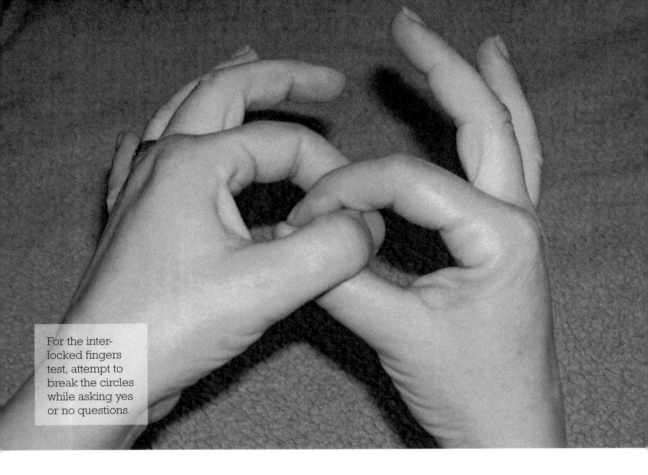

For the interlocked fingers test, attempt to break the circles while asking yes or no questions.

2. Now, make that same sign at the same time with your right hand, touching the thumb and first finger together. When you do this interlock the two circles. The thumb and first finger will be touching inside the circle already formed by your left hand.

The actual test:
1. Do your positive practice test first. This can be a "yes" or it can be the answer to a question you know the answer to. Think or say, "Show me a yes" or "My name is _____" (use your real name).
2. Attempt to break the circles and separate your hands by pulling your hands apart. Do not consciously open either circle. You are checking to see that the thumb/finger connection is holding strong in both hands, and holds strong as soon as you ask the question.
3. Now do your negative practice test. Think or say "show me a no" or think or say "My name is Santa Claus" (Note: If you are really Santa Claus, please use a different fake name).

Case History: Temi

Name: Temi

Age: Nursing-age kid

Symptoms: Overnight onset of diarrhea. Diarrhea is normal brown color; no foul odor, no mucous or blood, normal temperature, normal pink mucous membranes, normal capillary refill, eating/drinking normally

I'm here by myself, so I'm depending on one-person tests. Because I can easily hold Temi, I can choose surrogate testing or muscle testing and save dowsing for my backup if necessary. All my supplies are back at the house, so I am testing without product samples or a written list.

For this situation, I'm opting to use two-handed muscle tests while touching her. Reminder: A yes is the ring formed by my touching fingers staying strong. A no is the ring weakening and pulling apart.

Before I begin I clear my polarity and then hers, then I say a short prayer for guidance, asking for the greatest good for all involved. Now I can begin asking yes/no questions.

"Do I have permission to test Temi at this time?" Yes.

"Is this a virus?" No.

"Is this bacteria?" No.

"Is this a parasite?" Yes.

Okay, now I know I'm working with a parasite issue.

At this point I could just start asking what will clear the parasite issue, or I could start asking questions to narrow down which parasite Temi is dealing with. I actually do not need to know which parasite it is in order to figure out what item will clear the issue for her. Her body knows, and I simply need to tap into what her body already knows. I opt to go straight for what helps.

I know that in the past, several things have helped other goats with parasites. To determine if I am working with products I am familiar with, I begin by asking, "Is this a product I have used on my goats before?" Yes.

This is important. Every now and then I get the answer No, which means I'm about to be challenged to find lists of other parasite remedies that I have never worked with before and start testing them. This will occasionally happen to you also. But this time I got a Yes, so I know my list of possible solutions. Now I work my way through my mental list of possible products.

"Is Miracle Clay the remedy?" No.

"Is Dynamite Excel the remedy?" No.

"Is Dynamite Herbal Tonic the remedy?" No.

"Is Dynamite DynaPro the remedy?" No.

"Is diatomaceous earth the remedy?" No.

"Is fresh pumpkin seed the remedy?" No.

"Is Dynamite Trace Minerals Concentrate the remedy?" Yes!

I now have an answer to my remedy question. I retest once more just to make sure.

"Does Dynamite Trace Minerals Concentrate resolve this issue for Temi?" Yes.

Just to make extra sure, and because I'm a curious person, I will often add a variation to that question. I phrase the question differently so that if Trace Minerals Concentrate is the correct answer I would get a No.

"Is there another remedy besides Trace Minerals Concentrate that would work better?" No.

Now, and this is very important, I also ask "Can Temi tolerate Trace Minerals Concentrate at this time?" Yes.

If I had gotten a No, I would know that I need to keep looking for another remedy that tests Yes for clearing the issue and tolerating the remedy.)

Finally, in case there might be additional support that would help her overall health, I ask one more remedy question.

"Are there any other changes to her feeding or nutrition program that Temi needs at this time?" No.

If I had gotten a Yes, then I would need to repeat the entire process described before this question to narrow down the additional support her body needed.

Now that I have determined that the only change she needs is adding the Trace Minerals Concentrate, I have to figure out how much.

My preferred method is to use the one-handed or two-handed muscle test while touching her and start asking dose amounts, starting with the lowest dose. I know Trace Minerals Concentrate is given with a dropper, and the dose for a two hundred–pound person is typically twenty drops. That tells me to start asking in units of drops, and that it's likely I will be needing less than twenty.

I ask "More than one drop daily?" Yes

"More than two drops daily?" Yes.

"More than three drops daily?" Yes.

. . . And so on until I get to five. At "More than five drops daily?" I get No.

To confirm that dose I ask "Is five drops daily the correct dose of Trace Minerals Concentrate for Temi?" Yes.

Next, I determine how to administer the drops.

"Give the drops in her meal?" No.

"Give the drops separately?" Yes.

So, I have determined that Temi needs five drops of Trace Minerals Concentrate given daily separate from her meal.

If I'm totally unfamiliar with the product, I can ask questions about dilution, adding molasses, and any other details of the dosing.

Finally, I need to know how long to continue the drops.

"More than one day?" Yes.

"More than two days?" Yes.

. . . And so on until I got to "More than ten days?" No.

Now I confirm: "Is ten days the correct length of time to give Temi the Trace Minerals Concentrate?" Yes.

I wrap up the entire process with a final summary, just to make totally sure.

"Is five drops daily for ten days of Trace Minerals Concentrate given separately from a meal the best remedy for Temi at this time?" Yes.

In this particular case, I also tested and determined that Dynamite DynaPro prebiotic would be helpful support. I mixed DynaPro, Trace Minerals Concentrate, molasses, and water in a syringe and dosed Temi daily for ten days. In twenty-four hours her manure had firmed back up to pellets. I continued for the full ten days, even though the symptoms had resolved earlier, because muscle testing continued to indicate the need for a full ten days.

4. Attempt to break the circles and separate your hands by pulling your hands apart. Do not consciously open either circle. You are checking to see that the thumb/finger connection weakened in both hands, and the connection breaks as soon as you ask the question and pull. Your hands should separate.

You now have your baseline, and you know what a yes and a no feel like. Practice this with questions you know the answer to until you feel confident, then move into the actual testing.

For actual testing, you can ask yes or no questions about anything related to your goat, or even your entire herd as a whole. Some examples:

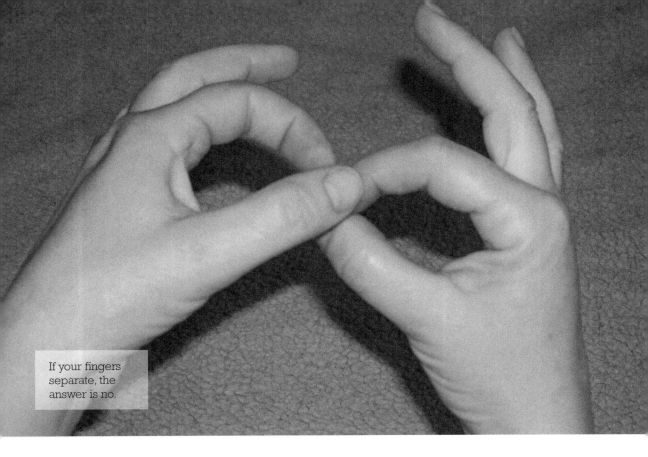

If your fingers separate, the answer is no.

- Does my goat need to be dewormed?
- Is diatomaceous earth the best dewormer for this goat at this time?
- Does my goat prefer a black feed bucket instead of a red feed bucket?
- Is this hay safe for my goat to eat?

Remember, your questions should be specific and only answered by yes or no.

Examples of questions to avoid:

- Which dewormer should I use? This is not a yes or no question
- Is this hay nutritious? This is too general even though it is a yes or no answer. Nutritious for which animal? Nutritious how? Be more specific.

There are literally thousands of possible remedies. Remedies could be herbs, supplements, bodywork, homeopathy, Reiki, essential oils, or flower essences to name some common categories. There are others. Additionally, it is possible to have more than one solution to an issue. Start with the remedies you are familiar with and test those. If none of those clear the point, start looking at the less familiar. You may need to dowse or muscle test to narrow down your list of possible candidates. With familiar remedies, you will probably already have a sense of what remedies could be useful. I have included a chart of possible remedies from Dynamite, Molly's Herbals, Land of Havilah, and Fir Meadow to get you started.

A Different Version of Interlocked Fingers
I'm again going to assume you are right-handed. Hang in there, left-handed folks—we'll do something just for you in a bit.

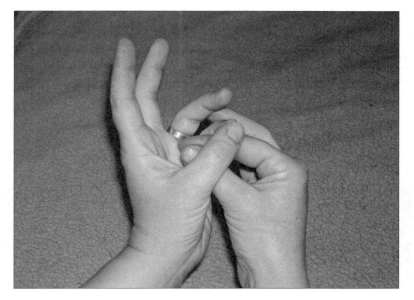

In an alternate version of the interlocked finger test, you will use the thumb and index finger of your right hand to attempt to pry open the circle of your left thumb and little finger.

The setup:
1. Touch your thumb and last finger of your left hand together at the tip to form a circle, like you are showing someone three fingers.
2. Now, with your right hand, touch the thumb and first finger together. Flatten out the circle that your thumb and finger form, like you are trying to pick up something tiny and fragile.
3. Place the thumb and first finger of your right hand inside the circle you made with your left hand's thumb and last finger.
4. Instead of pulling apart interlocking circles, you are going to use the fingers of your right hand to attempt to pry open the circle of your left fingers.

The actual test:

1. Do your positive practice test first. This can be a "yes" or it can be the answer to a question you know the answer to. Think or say, "Show me a yes" or "My name is _____" (use your real name).

2. Attempt to break the circle formed by your left thumb and pinky by prying it apart by opening your right thumb and first finger. You are checking to see that the left thumb/finger circle is holding strong and continues to hold strong as you answer the question.

3. Now do your negative practice test. Think or say, "Show me a no," or think or say, "My name is Santa Claus." (Note: If you are really Santa Claus, please use a different fake name.)

4. Attempt to break the circle formed by your left thumb and pinky by prying it apart by opening your right thumb and first finger. Do not consciously open the circle. You are checking to see that the left thumb/finger connection weakened, and the connection should break as soon as you ask the question and pry. Your left thumb and pinky should separate.

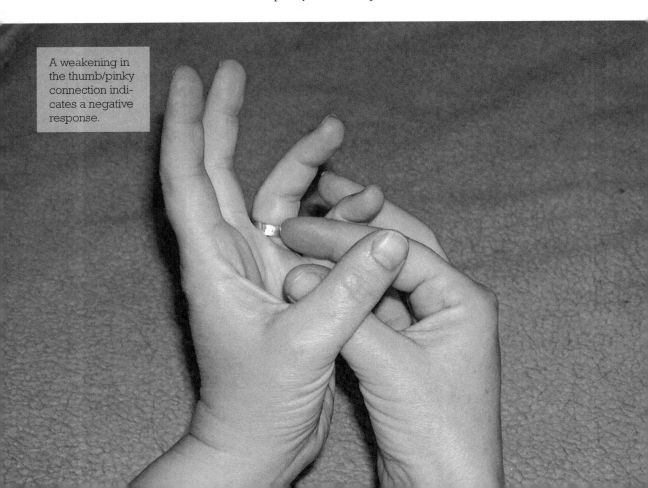

A weakening in the thumb/pinky connection indicates a negative response.

You now have your baseline and know what a yes and a no feel like. Practice this with questions you know the answer to until you feel confident, and then move into the actual testing.

One-Hand Finger Test

You can use either hand for this test, but for you lefties we'll switch things up and make this a left-handed test. The one-hand test is done differently than the two-hand tests. In two-hand tests, you are breaking a connection between fingers. In a single-hand test, you are looking at which fingers form a connection. The motion is similar to pinching something or grabbing a pencil. The setup is very important, as this determines your "yes" and "no." For me, my "yes" is my thumb and first finger coming together, and my "no" is my thumb and second and third fingers coming together.

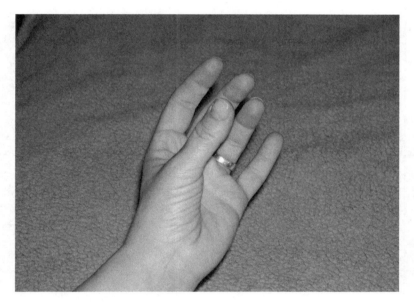

Under some circumstances, such as when you must keep hold of something with one hand, you may find it necessary to test using only one hand. Either hand may be used for this test.

The setup:
1. Hold your left hand partially closed, like you are preparing to grab something.

The actual test:
1. Do your positive practice test first. This can be a "yes" or it can be the answer to a question you know the answer to. Think or say, "Show me a yes" or "My name is _____" (use your real name).

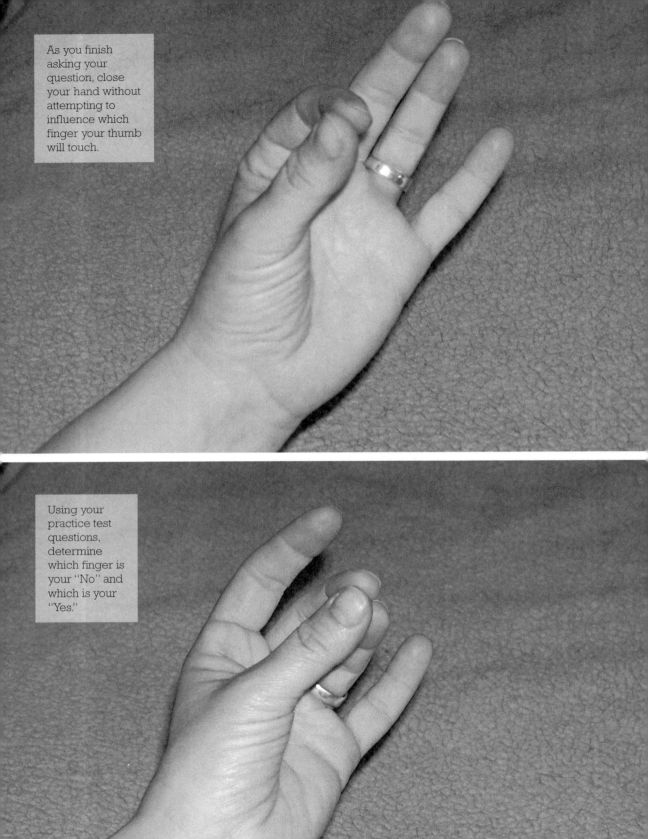

As you finish
asking your
question, close
your hand without
attempting to
influence which
finger your thumb
will touch.

Using your
practice test
questions,
determine
which finger is
your "No" and
which is your
"Yes."

2. As you are finishing your question, close your left hand. Do not attempt to influence which finger or fingers your thumb meets up with. Make note of which fingers are touching your thumb when your hand is closed. This is your "yes."

3. Now do your negative practice test. Think or say, "Show me a no" or "My name is Santa Claus" (this will not work if you are in fact named Santa Claus).

4. As you are finishing your question, close your left hand. Do not attempt to influence which fingers end up touching your thumb. Make note of which fingers touched this time. This is your "no."

You now have your baseline, and you know what a yes and a no feel like. Practice this with questions you know the answer to until you feel confident, and then move into the actual testing.

Blink Testing

This is a useful muscle test when both your hands are occupied holding a goat and a sample. The basic setup for blink testing or blink dowsing is to first establish your yes and no.

For me, my yes is a blink and my no is an unblinking stare.

I use my name to confirm the yes, and another name to confirm my no.

I say, "My name is Carrie," and immediately I feel the urge to blink, which I do.

Then I say "My name is _____," and there is no urge to blink, just a stare.

Once I have set up my yes and no, I can start asking yes-and-no questions about the goat.

The Push-Pull Test

I'm including this useful little technique here even though it does not provide answers to yes/no questions. This is a simple way to use your body to test whether a product is compatible with you or not. If you are touching your goat while performing the test, you can check compatibility with your goat. Contact is the key. If you are not touching the goat and are focused on yourself, you will get compatibility answers for yourself. If you touch the goat, you are picking up the goat's energy. Advanced user note: Remember contact *and* intent—both matter. If you are remote testing without touching the goat, think about the goat, picture the goat, be as specific mentally as possible, and you *can* use a push-pull test remotely to check compatibility with your goat. This is an advanced technique. Do not attempt until you are very confident with contact testing.

To get comfortable with the push-pull test, find yourself something you know would be toxic or incompatible with your body as well as a healthy piece of fruit or some clean water.

The setup:

1. Stand with your feet comfortably on the ground, separated by less than your shoulder width, toes pointing forward. Relax your knees.

Although the push-pull test cannot be used to answer yes-or-no questions, it is a useful technique to test whether a substance is compatible with you or not.

The test:

1. Hold the fruit or water against your solar plexus, which is just below your sternum.
2. Relax your body and allow the fruit or water to pull you into a forward lean, rocking your weight onto your toes. This is your "yes," this fruit or water is compatible with my body.
3. Now put the fruit or water down and instead hold the toxic item to your solar plexus.
4. Relax your body and allow the item to push you into a lean backwards, rocking you onto your heels. This is your "no," this toxic item is unhealthy for me.

Play with this until you can comfortably find that relaxed posture and feel the tug forward or the push backward. You can now use this to test any substance, evaluating how it agrees with your body by feeling the pull or push. Usually, although not always, an item that is toxic/disagreeable to your body will also be toxic/disagreeable to your goats.

Two-Person Tests

The Arm Test

This is actually the original traditional muscle test, first used on people hundreds of years ago. I find it's not especially practical when testing my goats because I am usually the only person out in the barnyard. Nevertheless, it's still a handy test to learn and fun to use when you have a second person to assist. This test can be used both for yes/no questions and for testing specific remedies and dosages. The "no" or rejection of an item or dosage will always be the arm going weak, and quickly.

The position:

Choose who is the tester (the person asking the questions) and who is the testee (the person representing the goat). The tester stands facing the testee with the right hand on the testee's left shoulder. The tester's left hand is touching the testee's right wrist, using only the first two fingers. The testee is standing facing the tester. The testee is holding his right arm straight out to the side laterally, elbow straight, wrist limp and relaxed so the hand dangles. This position isolates the shoulder muscles for more precise test results.

The setup:

Standing in the correct position, test the "yes" and "no." For yes, pick a test question with a known positive answer. The tester may ask the question out loud or silently in his/her mind. After asking the question, the tester says "hold strong" to warn the testee then pushes down on the testee's right arm at the wrist using only two fingers. The testee's arm should immediately hold strong and lock in the upright extended position.*

After asking the question, the tester uses two fingers to push down on the testee's right arm at the wrist.

If the testee's arm locks in the upright extended position, the answer is yes. If the testee's arm weakens and falls to her side, the answer is no.

---

* The arm staying strong means the arm locks firmly in place. This is not a contest of strength. Strength means an instant firming/locking of the muscles. If the arm bobbles, weakens, or drops it indicates a negative/no/weakened reaction.

For "no," pick a test question with a known negative answer. The tester may ask the question out loud or silently in his or her mind. After asking the question, the tester says, "Hold strong" to warn the testee, then pushes down on the testee's right arm at the wrist, using only two fingers. The testee's arm should weaken and drop. For some testees, this weakening is a pronounced bobble. For others, the arm goes limp and drops down entirely.

For clarity, repeat the yes/no set-up tests until you're clear on what the strong hold feels like compared to the weak hold.

If there is no difference between the set-up tests, refer back to the section on complicating factors in chapter 1.

The actual test for yes/no questions:

1. Stand in the correct positions. Make sure the testee is touching the goat with the left hand, a foot, a hip, or any body part that can be nudged up against the goat.

When testing your goats, make sure that the testee is in physical contact with the goat you are testing.

2. The tester may ask the yes or no question out loud or silently in his/her mind.
3. After asking the question, the tester says "hold strong" to warn the testee then pushes down on the testee's right arm at the wrist using only two fingers.
4. The testee's right arm will either hold strong and lock in the upright extended position or weaken and bobble or drop.

When using the two-person method to test for remedies, make sure the testee is touching the goat with her hip, leg, or foot, as she will be holding the remedy in her left hand and will thus be unable to keep hold of the goat with that hand.

The testee should hold the remedy against the goat with her left hand. Her right arm should be extended.

The actual test for remedies:

1. Stand in the correct positions. Make sure the testee is touching the goat with a foot, a hip, any body part that can be nudged up against the goat. The testee will not be able to touch the goat with the left hand, as that hand is needed to hold the remedy.

2. The testee should hold the remedy with the left hand, either against the testee's solar plexus or against the goat.

3. The tester may ask yes/no questions about the remedy out loud or silently in his or her mind. The tester may also skip the yes/no question, in which case the test is simply for whether or not the remedy is appropriate for that goat in general.

4. After asking the question (if there *is* a question), the tester says "hold strong" to warn the testee then pushes down on the testee's right arm at the wrist using only two fingers.
5. The testee's right arm will either hold strong and lock in the upright extended position or weaken and bobble or drop.

IMPORTANT

Remember to ask if the goat can tolerate the remedy at that time. A remedy can test well for a goat even though the goat is not quite ready to have that remedy.

There are literally thousands of possible remedies. Remedies could be herbs, supplements, bodywork, homeopathy, Reiki, essential oils, or flower essences to name some common categories. There are others. Additionally, it's possible to have more than one solution to an issue. Start with the remedies you are familiar with and test those. If none of those clear the point, start looking at the less familiar. You may need to dowse or muscle test to narrow down your list of possible candidates. With familiar remedies, you will probably already have a sense of what remedies could be useful. I have included a chart of possible remedies from Dynamite, Molly's Herbals, Land of Havilah, and Fir Meadow in chapter 9 to get you started.

The actual test for dosages:
1. Stand in the correct positions. Make sure the testee is touching the goat with a foot, a hip, or any body part that can be nudged up against the goat. The testee will not be able to touch the goat with the left hand, as that hand is needed to hold the remedy.
2. The testee should hold the remedy with the left hand, either against the testee's solar plexus or against the goat.
3. The tester should start by stating (not asking) out loud or silently the lowest reasonable starting dose.
4. After stating the dose, the tester says "hold strong" to warn the testee then, using only two fingers, pushes down on the testee's right arm at the wrist.
5. The testee's right arm will either hold strong and lock in the upright extended position or weaken and bobble or drop.
6. If the arm weakens, then state an even lower dose, backing the dose down in steps until you find a dose that allows the arm to hold strong.

7. If the arm stays strong, then state the next higher dose and retest. If the arm stays strong at that higher dose, state an even higher dose and retest again.

8. Continue increasing the dose statement and retesting until the tester reaches a dose that weakens the testee's arm. That indicates the tester has exceeded the preferred dose amount and should go with the next lowest amount.

Are There Other Muscle Tests?

In practice, there are probably as many muscle tests as you have muscles (and flexibility). The ones I described are the most commonly used, and generally the easiest to use while wrangling a goat.

SUGGESTION

When a maximum dosage has been found, continue testing increasing and decreasing amounts, using smaller units of measure, to further refine the dose. For example, if two capsules were too much (weakened the arm) and one capsule kept the arm strong, then test one and a half capsules.

How I Muscle Test My Goats

For me personally, I find I most often use the second variation of the one-person interlocked finger test, the one where I place my right thumb and first finger inside the circle formed by my left thumb and first finger. I use the interlocked rings less often, and the one-handed or blink test even less often. If I need a hand free to hold the goat, I most often use blink testing, or I use distance muscle-testing to free up both hands.

3

What Are Reflex Points?

Chi, or qi (pronounced "key"), is energy that flows along meridians that connect all the organs in the body. Meridians are like blood vessels except composed of energy rather than being solid and visible. Qi flows to balance and nourish the organs and systems of the body. The smallest unit of qi energy is called a qion. A qion is actually described in quantum physics, referred to as a phonon, a quasiparticle used to calculate the vibrational properties of solids. Yes, energy medicine really does have a connection to science and physics, only now truly becoming understood. When the flow of qi is out of balance, blocked, or accelerated, the function of the organs and systems along that meridian will be affected. By studying known acupressure points along the meridians in bodies with known medical conditions, body workers have been able to figure out which points are good indicators of issues in different organs and systems. The human reflex points were documented by Dr. M. L. Rees (1920–1992). I have included the chart of the points he located on humans. We will refer back to this chart later in the book.

Reflex points are the simplest form of testing. You simply find the point and press gently. If it hurts, there is an issue. Very sensitive testers will learn to feel a congestion in the energy at the point before you actually press. Your fingers will start to be drawn to points as you become more attuned to the energy. For beginners, simply checking for pain is enough. Often the point will feel thickened or knotted as well, though not always. There are points for organs, such as the liver point. There are points for specific nutrients, such as the point for B vitamins. There is a point for dehydration. Your ability to test is only limited by the points that have been documented. For any organs or issues not charted as points you will have to use one of the muscle testing or dowsing techniques instead.

To check what product resolves the issue, find the sore point. Then hold the product against the body and recheck the point. If it no longer hurts, you have found the solution. If the pain continues or gets worse, keep testing products.

In the case of minerals that can be overdosed, especially potentially toxic minerals like selenium, you will need to check two points. For example, here is how to work with the selenium point:

First, check the selenium point. If it is sore, you could have an excess or a deficiency. Then check the liver point. You will have two possible scenarios.

Scenario one: The liver point is not sore. This is the simplest to test and resolve. If you found a sore selenium point and a clear liver point, then you are dealing with selenium deficiency and you simply test products until you find the one that clears the selenium point.

Scenario two: Your selenium point *and* your liver point are sore. Two different things may be going on here. If the selenium point and the liver point are both sore, you may have a toxicity issue and actually need to reduce selenium. The other possibility is that you have something else stressing the liver at the same time that you have a selenium deficiency. So, the two sore points may be linked, or there may be two separate issues affecting these points.

To figure out which possibility you are dealing with, focus on the liver for now and ignore the selenium point for a few minutes. Test products until you find what clears the liver. Then go back and test that product on the selenium point. If it clears the selenium point as well as the liver point, then you know it was selenium toxicity, and you know how to fix it. If the product

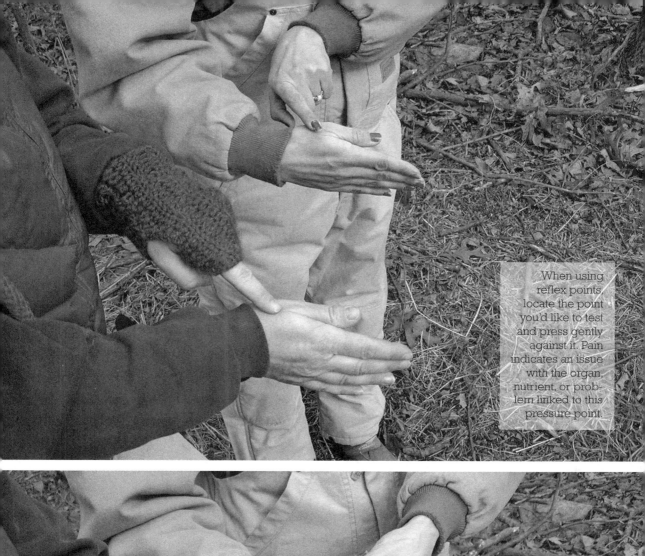

When using reflex points, locate the point you'd like to test and press gently against it. Pain indicates an issue with the organ, nutrient, or problem linked to this pressure point.

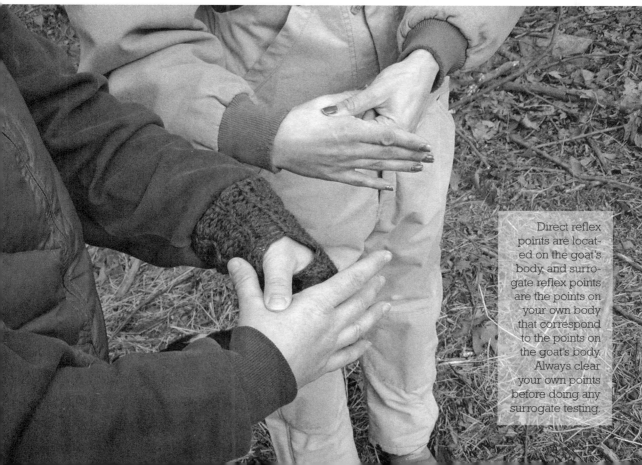

Direct reflex points are located on the goat's body, and surrogate reflex points are the points on your own body that correspond to the points on the goat's body. Always clear your own points before doing any surrogate testing.

clears the liver point but *not* the selenium point, then you know you have two different issues. At that point, test individually for what clears each point.

What Is the Difference between Direct and Surrogate Reflex Points?

Direct reflex points are located on the goat's body, and you test these points by touching them on the goat. Surrogate reflex points are the points on your own body that match points on the goat's body. If you touch the goat, then your body picks up the goat's energy. Your own reflex points then become "empathetic" with the goat's reflex points, meaning that they will show the same stresses. Surrogate testing uses your own body's reflex points to stand in for the goat's reflex points. Very important note: Always check your own points to make sure they are clear before doing surrogate tests. If your point is already active, you will not get an accurate surrogate test for the goat. If you find active points on your own body, test to find what product or therapy clears your point and postpone your surrogate testing until your own points are healthy.

Do Reflex Points Really Work?
Does Surrogate Testing Really Work?
How Is that Possible?

Living beings have an actual energy field surrounding them, called an aura or etheric field. This field can be seen using Kirlian photography, and some people can see it with the naked eye. Energy also has a vibrational frequency, similar to a sound wave. Energy can travel great distances (think cell phone signals, extremely low-frequency communications in submarines, and data transmissions from satellites in space). Many believe the energy frequency of a living being can also travel great distances,

Case History: Lexie

Name: Lexie
Age/Sex: Adult doe
Symptoms: Skin condition, weight loss, dry sparse hair coat, normal temperature, normal pink mucous membranes, normal capillary refill, eating/drinking normally, normal bowel movements

I'm here by myself, so I'm depending on one-person tests. Because I can easily hold Lexie, I can choose surrogate testing or muscle testing, and I can save dowsing for my backup if necessary. All my supplies are back at the house, so I am testing without product samples or a written list.

For this situation, I'm opting to use surrogate reflex tests while touching the goat because they are most immune to influence from my thoughts, and I'm quite concerned about getting accurate results because Lexie's skin issue is spreading rapidly. I have a chart of human reflex points that I keep handy out in the pasture or barn in case I need to look up one of the less common points.

I first clear my polarity and hers before saying a short prayer for guidance, asking for the greatest good for all involved. I then ask my first yes/no question *using two hands*:

Do I have permission to test Lexie at this time? Yes.

Even though I am working with some sort of skin issue and something related to digestion, I will test all the major reflex points that correspond to the healing priority list in the book. To test these points on the goat, I will gently press against the corresponding points on my body. If I feel a pain or soreness in that spot, I note it.

Liver: clear	Descending colon: clear
Blood sugar: clear	Thyroid: clear
Stomach: clear	Adrenals: clear
Heart: clear	Kidneys: clear
Virus: ouch!	Uterus: clear
Bacteria: sore	Ovaries: clear
Ascending colon: clear	

Note: There is no human reflex point for parasites, so I use a two-handed muscle test for parasites. She is clear—no parasites. I have now identified two points that are sore: Virus and bacteria.

At this point I could just start asking what clears the virus and bacteria issues, or I could start asking questions to narrow down which viruses and bacteria are affecting the goat. I don't actually need to know which specific virus or bacterium I'm dealing with in order to determine what item will clear the issues for her. In fact, the list of possible viruses and bacteria is huge. Lexie's body knows, and that is enough. I simply need to tap into what her body already knows. I opt to go straight for what helps clear the points.

I know that in the past, several things have helped other goats with a virus or bacteria challenge. I know that colloidal silver, tea tree oil, vitamin C in various forms, copper, and Dynamite Trace Minerals Concentrate (not available from any other company) are all possibilities for treatment. If experience had not told me that these are possible remedies, I would use the reference chart in the back of the book or look up those issues in a goat care book to see what remedies are suggested.

One by one, I hold the remedies against Lexie with one hand and check the virus point then the bacteria point with my other hand. I test every remedy against both points. I am looking for the remedy that makes the point stop hurting, and the best scenario is a remedy that makes both points stop hurting.

Colloidal silver
Virus: ouch
Bacteria: clear

Well, silver cleared one point so I set silver aside as a possible remedy to be used along with a second as-yet-unknown remedy.

Dynamite Trace Minerals Concentrate (TMC)
Virus : clear
Bacteria: clear

Aha! TMC cleared both points. This is a better solution than finding a second remedy to mix with the silver. To make doubly sure, I switch over to two-handed muscle testing for a moment.

"Is TMC the best remedy for Lexie for both the virus and the bacteria?" Yes.

"Is there another single remedy that would be a better choice?" No.

This answer is important. This tells me I can save time and skip testing all the other potential remedies.

And now for the *most* important question. Always ask this!

"Can Lexie tolerate TMC at this time?" Yes.

If I had gotten a no, I would know that I need to keep looking for another remedy that tests as clearing the virus point. Remember, I already asked if there was another possible single remedy for both and got no. So my only other option is to look for a remedy to clear the virus point in conjunction with using silver to clear the bacteria point.

Finally, in case there might be additional support that would help her overall health, I ask one more remedy question using two-handed muscle testing.

"Are there any other changes to her feeding or nutrition program that Lexie needs at this time?" No.

If I had gotten a Yes, then I would need to repeat the entire process described before this question to narrow down the additional support her body needed.

Now that I have determined that the only change she needs is adding the Trace Minerals Concentrate, I have to figure out how much. My preferred method for this is to use the one-handed or two-handed muscle test while touching her and start asking dose amounts, starting with the lowest dose. I know Trace Minerals Concentrate is given with a dropper, and the dose for a two-hundred-pound person is typically twenty drops. That tells me to start asking in units of drops, and it's likely I will end up needing fewer than twenty drops.

"More than one drop daily?" Yes.

"More than two drops daily?" Yes.

"More than three drops daily?" Yes.

. . . And so on until I get to five. At "More than five drops daily?" I get no.

To confirm that dose I ask "Is five drops daily the correct dose of Trace Minerals Concentrate for Lexie?" Yes.

Next I determine how to administer the drops.

"Give the drops in her meal?" Yes

So, I have determined that Lexie needs five drops of Trace Minerals Concentrate given daily in her meal.

Finally I need to know how long to continue the drops.

"More than one day?" Yes.

"More than two days?" Yes.

...And so on until I get to "More than seventeen days?" No.

Now I confirm: "Is seventeen days the correct length of time to give Lexie the Trace Minerals Concentrate?" Yes.

I wrap up the entire process with a final summary, just to make totally sure.

"Is five drops daily for seventeen days of Trace Minerals Concentrate given in a meal the best remedy for Lexie at this time?" Yes.

and logic and physics back this up. When two bodies are brought into contact with each other, or even into each other's energetic fields, one body is able to sense the energies of the other body.

How I Use Reflex Points for My Goats

I have memorized the basic reflex points for humans, and I have a chart of the points I check less often. I find it easier to use my surrogate points rather than testing the goat's own reflex points. The majority of the organ systems match up, other than my stomach being different from the goat's four-chambered stomach (omasum, abomasum, reticulum, rumen).

The actual test for dosages:

1. I check all my own points. If any of my points are reactive, I will not use that point for testing the goat (and I make mental note to test what clears that point and address the issue in my own body).

2. I make physical contact with my goat, usually just leaning a hip against them or touching them with a hand. Often, I just nudge my foot up against my goat's hoof.

3. I check each of my own points while touching the goat, making note of which points are reactive.

4. For any points that are reactive, I hold the appropriate remedy against the goat and recheck my point, until I find the remedy that clears my surrogate point. This tells me which remedy will assist the goat.

5. For points that do not match up, mainly the stomach, I switch to surrogate muscle testing or surrogate dowsing.

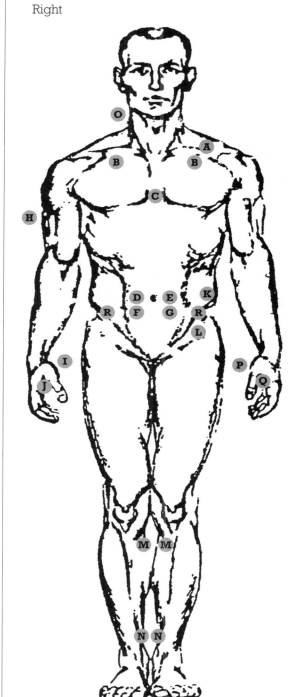

A. Calcium (roll left shoulder
   forward. Point is on bone on
   back side of clavicle)

B. Lung (just below the clavicle
   at midpoint)

C. Virus (on sternum at pre-gravity
   nipple line)

D. Magnesium (right one inch
   from navel)

E. Manganese (left one inch
   from navel)

F. Zinc (right one inch to the side
   and one inch down from navel)

G. Copper (left one inch to the side
   and one inch down from navel)

H. Bacteria (middle of belly of
   triceps)

I. Pancreas and blood sugar (base
   of thumb on phenar pad)

J. Liver (proximal end of crease of
   web between thumb and finger
   — see book photo)

K. Selenium (on left side on last
   rib)

L. B vitamins (from point of left
   hip one inch toward midline
   and one inch down)

M. Ovaries/testes (on inner side
   of tibia where bone starts to
   curve)

N. Uterus/prostate (four fingers
   width above the ankle bone)

O. Thyroid (back of neck on 5th
   cervical vertebra)

P. Heart (base of thumb on phenar
   pad)

Q. Stomach (proximal end of
   crease of web between thumb
   and finger)

R. Kidneys (one inch toward
   midline from point of hip on
   both sides)

When surrogate testing, make sure that you are in contact with the goat as you test the reflex points.

Remedies: There are literally thousands of possible remedies. Remedies could be herbs, supplements, bodywork, homeopathy, Reiki, essential oils, or flower essences to name some common categories. There are others. Additionally, it's possible to have more than one solution to an issue. Start with the remedies you are familiar with and test those. If none of those clear the point, start looking at the less familiar. You may need to dowse or muscle test to narrow down your list of possible candidates. With familiar remedies, you will probably already have a sense of what remedies could be useful. In chapter 9 I have included a chart of possible remedies from Dynamite, Molly's Herbals, Land of Havilah, and Fir Meadow to get you started.

If I find multiple reflex points that are reactive, I look for the product or therapy that clears the greatest number of points. There is also a priority order to the reflex points. If I cannot

CAUTION

If your reflex point is already stressed, it will not accurately reflect the stress on the goat's point. Always check and clear your own points before doing surrogate testing.

clear them all with one product, I focus on clearing the most important points first. The order of priority from highest to lowest is:

- Virus
- Bacteria
- Liver
- Heart
- Stomach/pancreas
- Kidney
- Adrenal
- Hormones/ reproductive points
- Specific vitamins/ minerals

4

What Is Dowsing?

Dowsing is based on the same energy principles as muscle testing. The difference is that muscle testing uses muscle responses while dowsing involves dowsing tools that are moved by energy and intent. The most common image of dowsing that most people hold is of the "water witch" carrying a forked stick to dowse for water when digging a well. In reality, folks dowse for water with forked sticks, two sticks held parallel and loosely, paired copper rods, pendulums, and probably many other tools I have not yet run across. I use the pendulum for my goat dowsing work (and save the copper rods for hunting ley lines and geopathic stress zones). I have seen dowsers use dowsing rods on people and animals to locate issues. I just find the rods less convenient when working with animals.

Choosing Your Pendulum

A pendulum can be as simple as a heavy nut or washer tied to one end of a foot of fishing line or string or as fancy as a crystal or metal pendulum hung from a thong or chain. Pendulums come as shaped crystals, uncut crystals, solid metal teardrops or cylinders, or even hollow metal pendulums that you can insert testing substances into. The most common use would be to insert a sample of hair from the goat inside the pendulum. Hint: If you buy a hollow pendulum, make sure the opening is large enough to easily remove whatever you insert. Many are not. My favorite pendulum design is a crystal on a chain that can be worn as a necklace, then unfastened and used for dowsing. To pick out your own pendulum, should you choose to purchase rather than make one, simply trust your intuition about the design that you are drawn to. Or you can use push-pull testing, holding the pendulum to your solar plexus, to find the pendulum that strongly draws you forward.

Using Your Pendulum

Hold the pendulum chain firmly between your thumb and first finger. I like to drape the chain over my middle finger rather than let it hang straight down. Work with what feels best to you. Allow enough length of chain for the pendulum to swing freely. Depending on the weight of your pendulum and the type of chain, you will have to experiment to find the length that al-

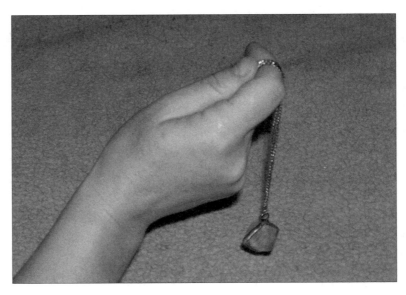

Dowsing tools come in all shapes and sizes, but one of the most common is the pendulum.

Case History: Entire Doe Herd

Sometimes you will want to ask questions that cover the herd as a group, rather than dealing with an individual goat. At other times, nothing is wrong and you simply want to check in to see if anything in your program could be improved.

This example tackles both scenarios while illustrating how to dowse using lists.

Spring had arrived and the doe herd had been out grazing for a couple weeks. Everyone appeared to be healthy and in good weight with no obvious issues. Because the weather and the feed had both changed, this felt like a good time to check in and see if I needed to make any changes to the overall doe program. It was a rainy day, so I worked indoors away from the herd. I chose to dowse.* For me when I dowse, No is a forward-and-back swing and Yes is a clockwise circle. I also close my eyes while asking each question so that I do not attempt to influence the motion.

When I began to set up, I grabbed my pendulum, a notepad and pen for taking notes, and my Dynamite product catalog. If I were new to this process, I might have also obtained a hair sample from each doe, mixed them together, and placed them either in a hollow pendulum or on the table where I was dowsing.

I started my dowsing session by clearing my polarity. Then I said my prayer asking for the greatest good.

My first question was "Do I have permission to do this dowsing at this time?" Yes. If no, I would have asked questions to figure out why not and when would be a better time to dowse.

I knew I wanted to check on the herd's hay, the amount of time they were spending on pasture, and their supplements. I also wanted to check on whether it was time to do a herd-wide detoxification or a herd-wide deworming. Here is my question list:

"Is their current hay meeting their needs?" Yes.

"Do I need to change their current hay type?" No.

"Do I need to change their current hay amount?" No.

"Are they getting enough time on pasture?" No.

"Is their current feeding program compensating for the lack of pasture?" Yes.

"Are they getting too much time on pasture?" No.

---

* As you get more confident, you will find you can use muscle testing or even surrogate points remotely. This is an advanced technique. Start with the approach you feel confident using.

"Does the pasture need to be rotated?" No.

So far, so good—everything can stay the same.

"Is their current supplement program optimum for the herd?" No.

Notice that I could have phrased that last question differently and gotten a Yes that would have also indicated a change is needed.

"Does their current supplement program need to be changed?" Yes.

So I learned that I can improve their supplement program by changing it.

Next I had to determine if the necessary change can be achieved by adding a supplement or removing a supplement or just changing a dose.

"Do I need to stop using one of the supplements?" No.

"Do I need to start using a new supplement?" Yes.

"Do I need to change the dose of an existing supplement?" No.

So I knew I'd be adding something to their existing program. At this point I knew it was time to get out my Dynamite product list and start dowsing. Although I could ask yes/no for every item on the list, to save time I divided the list into sections instead. I asked if the new product was in each section, then narrowed it down from there. I worked my way through the list, product section by product section, until I narrowed down that I needed to add Dynamite Excel topdressed on their daily meal. I confirmed the dosage also.

I then asked, "Are there any other additions the doe herd needs at this time?" No.

Finally, I asked, "Can all the does tolerate this change?" Yes. Always always always ask this question.

Remember, I had also wanted to check on detoxification and deworming.

"Does the doe herd need a detoxification?" Yes.

Hah! Now because I know a bit about Dynamite Excel, I knew it sometimes tests well for detoxification, which led to my next question.

"Does Excel resolve the doe's need for detoxification?" Yes!

"Do the does need a detoxification product besides Excel at this time?" No.

More confirmation that I'm getting appropriate answers.

My last question concerned parasites.

"Do the does need to be dewormed?" Maybe.

Wait, what? Maybe?

Sometimes when you dowse, your pendulum will either refuse to swing or it will make some odd, random motions showing neither yes nor no. This is a clue that you need to make your question more specific in some way.

In this case, I suspected that perhaps some does needed to be dewormed and some were currently in balance with their parasite load. I asked the question a different way.

"Do some of the does need to be dewormed?" Yes.

Aha!

Knowing that Excel contains clay and diatomaceous earth, and knowing that earlier I dowsed that the does only needed one product added to their program, I had a suspicion as to where my next questions would lead, but I asked anyway.

"Will the Excel resolve the parasite issue for the does that currently need deworming?" Yes.

If I had gotten a No, then I would know that something in my previous questions was incorrect. I would go back to the beginning and recheck my permissions. I would recheck my polarity. I would check where I was sitting and make sure there weren't any strong electrical fields that could interfere with my results. I would take a drink of water and maybe some electrolytes.

In conclusion, for this particular testing session, I determined that the does needed Excel added to their daily grain. Everyone already looked very healthy and had no symptoms, so making the change did not produce obvious changes. I trusted the testing and that the does did indeed need that change at that time.

---

lows the easiest, freest movement. I close my eyes while asking my questions to make sure I am not influencing the answer. You can speak or think your questions. You do not need to be in actual contact with the remedy, list, or goat. Some folks prefer

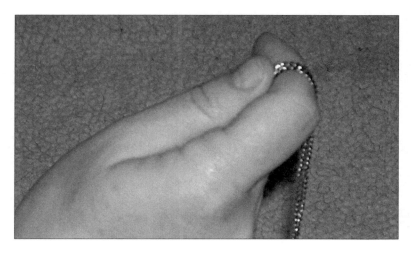

You may need to experiment a little to determine what length of chain allows for the freest movement of your pendulum.

to take a sample of the goat's hair and put it in the pendulum or near the pendulum. Some folks prefer to have a photograph of the goat. You can use the pendulum without either. If you are struggling to get clear answers, a hair sample or photo can focus your results. You do not need to stop the pendulum's movement between questions, although you can. If you leave the pendulum in motion, allow the full thirty seconds for the movement pattern to shift if it is going to.

Your first step is the same as muscle testing. Say a prayer, talk to your angels, use an affirmation—whatever your personal faith indicates. Ask for the greatest good and for God, angels, white light—however you view the positive elements of the spirit—to surround and protect your work. Next you will need to establish your yes and no. For me, yes is a clockwise circle, and no is a forward-and-back swing. If in doubt, say, "Show me a yes" with your eyes closed, give it thirty seconds, then observe how your pendulum is moving. Then close your eyes and say, "Show me a no," and after thirty seconds observe the movement. Ask some test questions to make sure of your yes and no. Once you have your yes and no figured out, those will likely continue to be your yes and no for all time. I still go through the confirmation process every time I dowse to strengthen my answers and strengthen my faith in the results.

Does Dowsing Work?

The same principles and warnings that apply to muscle testing also apply to dowsing. Dowsing works. Dowsing has been used for hundreds of years to locate water and for other purposes.

How I Dowse to Help My Goats

I use dowsing the same way I use muscle testing, and I use dowsing for everything from supplements to feed to asking health questions to choosing the best color bucket. I will especially use dowsing when I prefer to work indoors in the comfort of my home. I also use dowsing when I need to ensure that my mind is not influencing my answers. If I start muscle testing and feel that perhaps I am influencing the answers because of a personal preference, I will switch to dowsing with my eyes closed. If I cannot see how the pendulum is swinging, I cannot influence the swing. I use dowsing only for yes or no questions and to narrow down lists.

Some Advantages to Dowsing

With dowsing, you can quickly work your way through lists. Lists of supplements, lists of illnesses, lists of remedies, any list you can think of. Dowse by section. For example, if I have three columns of possible supplements, I can dowse which column to look in, then which section, and in that way quickly narrow a list of fifty down to a couple of choices, much faster than muscle testing fifty items individually.

Another advantage, as I mentioned previously, is that I cannot influence the results if I close my eyes.

5

Putting It All Together

The Setup

Before beginning, I must decide which test I am using: muscle testing, reflex points, or dowsing. I gather up any product samples, lists of supplements, or the cross-reference chart from this book. I find a volunteer if I am doing two-person testing. I round up my goat. I get a notepad to record my answers. If I am doing distance testing or dowsing, I may collect a hair sample from the goat.

Questions

I start with a quick prayer and blessing. Many folks skip this step. I personally feel more comfortable asking for the session to be blessed and stating my willingness to serve the greatest good. Then I clear my polarity and the goat's polarity. I ask two questions:

Do I have permission to test this goat?

Is testing this goat for the greatest good?

If the answer is "no" to either of these, I stop right here and come back another time.

If the answer to both of these questions is "yes," I move into doing the actual tests.

Pay attention to the obvious. If your normally friendly goat refuses to be caught, walks away, or otherwise resists, it may be that you don't have permission to do this work on that goat at this time.

I ask questions to narrow down the issue.

I ask questions to identify solutions.

I ask questions to clarify dosages (if giving a supplement or remedy), potencies, and length of treatment.

I *always* ask if the goat can tolerate the supplement or remedy or therapy. This is especially important with the very young and very old and debilitated animals.

Easy-to-assemble testing kit. The box is a school supply box. The tiny sample containers are available online in bulk and used for holding cosmetics. Five gram size.

Complications

If at any point in the process I start to get conflicting answers, or unclear answers, I refer back to the sections on polarity, hydration, and other complicating factors in chapter 1. I clear my polarity and the goat's polarity again. I recheck my yes and no responses with a simple name question, using my name and a wrong name. I review my motivation for doing the testing and ask again that the results be for the greatest good.

I may switch my testing method. Reflex points and dowsing are the least likely to be influenced by my personal opinions and preferences. If the answers are still inconsistent, I walk away and pick up the testing another time.

TIP

Be sure to keep these items handy when checking up on your herd
- Pen or pencil
- Notepad
- Testing kit if you have one

Optional
- Charts, books, or lists of remedies to test
- Pendulum if you plan to test near your goat
- This book

6

Making the Transition to Holistic

Many of you reading this book plan to use these techniques to switch your goat herd over to more holistic management practices. There is a right way and a wrong way to make the switch. If you make a cold-turkey switch to entirely holistic methods overnight, you may be risking a sick or dead goat. Just as you would allow a goat time to adjust to a new climate or feed, you must allow time for the body to adjust to the new program. After going through this transition process many times, both with my own and with clients' goats, I've come up with a somewhat standardized approach. Before making drastic changes to your goat's management program, it's always a good idea to talk to a trusted health professional.

Overall, the holistic Eastern approach to goat health depends on the goat's own immune system. The focus is on health maintenance and disease prevention rather than disease management and crisis intervention. While the reference table in chapter 9 includes many diseases, my hope is that as your herd gets healthier you will need to refer to that table less and less often. That has been the case for my herd. To get you to that optimum health, I have laid out a series of steps taken over a two-year period to make the full transition. Yes, two years is the total amount of time. While you will see changes much sooner, of course, all of the changes to bone, soft tissue, organs, and energy can take up to two years.

Step 1, the first month: This first step assumes the goats have been getting the typical commercial grain mix. These mixes usually contain preservatives, flavorings, unusable minerals, by-products, meals, mineral oil, lots of sugar, and other ingredients that lead to health challenges such as liver toxicity, kidney stress, changes to DNA, abscesses, hair loss, and many other symptoms. To begin making the transition, over the course of a couple weeks, I start cutting the commercial grain mix with more natural substitutes. There are almost as many ways to mix and match grains as there are goat folks. To some extent your choices depend on your hay and browse situation as well as the season. Possible substitutes include oats, non-GMO corn, barley, organic black oil sunflower seeds (BOSS), and non-GMO alfalfa hay or pellets. Keep the total amount of concentrates fed equal by weight to the amount of the commercial mix, and only start cutting back the total weight fed after the transition to natural substitutes is complete and the goats have been eating their new food for a couple weeks. I use a good prebiotic/probiotic during this process.

Generally speaking, focus on high-fat ingredients for healthy weight and grains for extra energy. Remember, grains are for energy, fats are for weight gain, and alfalfa and soy are muscle/topline builders and protein boosters, so consider your feeding goals when formulating. Peas are another good protein source. In general, the less grain you can feed while still maintaining weight, growth rates, and milk yield, the better. The best feed

> **"But my goat is totally healthy and has none of those symptoms. Maybe I don't need to change anything."**
>
> Does your goat need to be dewormed more than a couple times a year? Have you had any issues with conception, carrying to term, or having only one kid? Ever have pneumonia or other illnesses during winter? Have you had to intervene with drugs or medications? If the answer is yes to any of these, I would argue that your goat in fact is *not* healthy. A healthy body fights off parasites and illnesses and reproduces easily and abundantly.

for goats is still what nature intended, a varied browse diet on healthy soils.

Some thoughts to consider when making your personal mix:

- In Eastern medicine, foods are considered to either cool or warm the body. I am not talking about a temperature you can measure with a thermometer. This warming or cooling is energetic and part of the overall energetic balance of the body. Oats are a warming grain and barley cooling, so you may want to switch off depending on the time of year.
- Alfalfa or alfalfa pellets will be high calcium and high protein, and I consider alfalfa more of a supplement than a feed in general (I know many dairy folks consider alfalfa a main part of the diet, so my perspective is a bit different). I feel there are usually ways to support dairy goats without alfalfa. When in doubt, muscle test what works best for *your* herd.
- Non-GMO corn is a fantastic grain, if you can find it. Corn is very warming and very high calorie. Always use whole corn, as cracked or flaked corn can be at risk for mold unless dried very carefully. My experience has been that few mills take the care necessary to properly dry corn and resort to (toxic) mold inhibitors as a less expensive solution.
- The simplest recipe is using corn/oats/barley in equal amounts by weight, then add BOSS and alfalfa as needed to maintain body condition and milk production.

BOSS is good for laying down body fat. Start with a handful of organic BOSS* and evaluate your goats' body condition. Increase as needed until body fat is correct. In general, wild goats will not have much fat in their diet, so I keep this in mind when adding BOSS. If you are not familiar with how to evaluate body condition, a multitude of videos, pictures, and articles on the internet explain how to score body condition in dairy and meat goats. There is a difference between scoring the two categories, so know which body type your goat is before evaluating. In general, body condition scoring evaluates both fat and muscle cover. It takes about six weeks to transition between score numbers. The score ranges from 1 to 5, with 1 being emaciated and 5 being overconditioned. Numbers of 3 and 4 are in the healthy

---

* The herbicide glyphosate was approved as a desiccant for sunflowers, oats, and barley. Use only organic or muscle test for glyphosate residue.

range. Condition is evaluated by feeling the ribs, the spine, the sternum, and the transverse processes over the loins. If you are not familiar with scoring, I suggest doing some internet research.

I add non-GMO alfalfa and/or non-GMO whole extruded soy if muscle is lacking. The alfalfa rule of thumb in my barn is never go above 10 percent by weight of the entire daily browse/hay ration. If I have to go higher than that, something is wrong somewhere else in my feeding or supplement program.

Any of these suggestions for simple grains and alfalfa assume that you are feeding a high-quality vitamin mineral supplement. Do *not* assume a simple grain blend will meet all your goats' nutritional needs. The vitamin and mineral content of any feed depends on the health of the soil it is grown in, and soils vary widely. Many soils are mineral depleted.

Many different rules of thumb have been published on how much grain to feed and how to balance a ration. A simple internet search will locate many options. Keep in mind that all the ration balance calculators depend on averages and results of feeding studies, and in my opinion there is just no way to truly represent every goat and every feed. Hay will vary from bale to

Emaciated and weak animal: the backbone is highly visible and forms a continuous ridge. The flank is hollow. Ribs are clearly visible. There is no fat cover and fingers easily penetrate into intercostal spaces (between ribs).

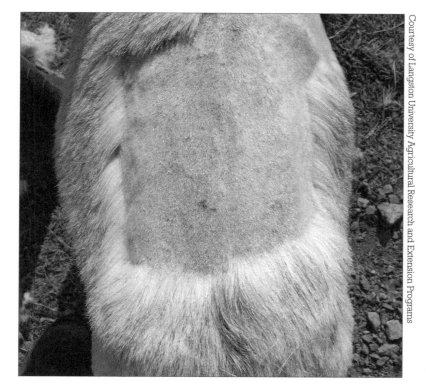

Slightly raw-boned: the backbone is still visible with a continuous ridge. Some ribs can be seen and there is a small amount of fat cover. Ribs are still felt. Intercostal spaces are smooth but can still be penetrated.

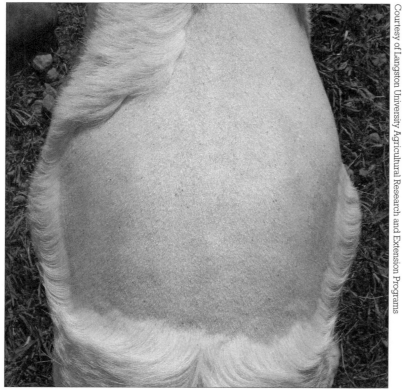

The backbone is not prominent. Ribs are barely discernible; an even layer of fat covers them. Intercostal spaces are felt using pressure.

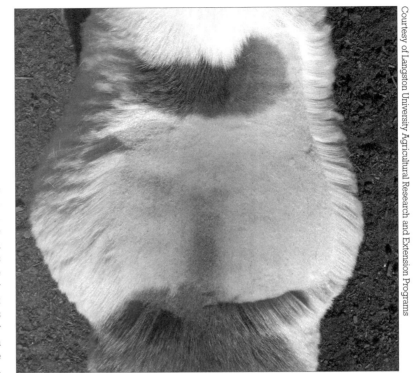

The backbone
cannot be seen.
Ribs are not seen.
The side of the
animal is sleek in
appearance. This
photo is an example
of body scoring for
meat goats only.
Because of less
muscle mass, dairy
goats will have a
visible bone frame
at this score.

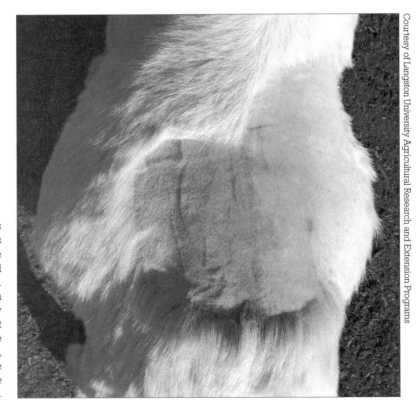

The backbone is
buried in fat. Ribs
are not visible. The
rib cage is covered
with excessive fat.
This photo is an
example of body
scoring for meat
goats only. Because
of less muscle mass,
dairy goats will have
a visible bone frame
at this score.

bale and batch to batch. Grain will vary depending on where in the field it was grown. My experience is that the quality of hay and browse, the mineral content and quality of grain, the needs of the goat, the breed of the goat, and individual goat variations are all so different that using a calculator and attempting to balance math will drive you quietly insane and still may not help you meet every goat's needs. A ration calculator could give you a starting point, and then you could use energy testing to tweak the results. I personally don't use a ration balance calculator at all. I start with the best hay and browse possible, then add basic broad-spectrum supplements, and then adjust fats and grains to get the body score into the healthy range. Finally, offering free-choice supplements allows your goats to do any fine balancing beyond what you can do with testing.

Step 2, months two through five: In months two through five, you have a decision to make about the health priorities of your herd. Beforehand, make any adjustments that you must to maintain your goat's healthy weight. Then you will need to make a decision between starting to rebuild mineral reserves and doing a full-body cleanse or detoxification (detox). This is a judgment call and unique to each goat.

Typically if the herd has a significant history of exposure to chemical dewormers, lice medicine, herbicides, pesticides, or toxic water, I muscle test or dowse the goat to start with detoxification. Remember, always ask if the goat can tolerate the change. The other option indicated by muscle testing or dowsing in month two is starting the rebuilding process with a high-quality vitamin/mineral supplement program and wait to start a detox. Again, ask if the goat can tolerate the change. Remember: the body does not clean house and rebuild at the same time. Dowse or muscle test to pick a path for month two, and pick only one path.

If you start with the detox, there is another decision to muscle test or dowse. How toxic are the goats? If you suspect high levels of toxin exposure, or you don't know, detox is usually most safely done by starting with a mild, conservative detoxification agent and building up from there. The most conservative gentle detox is montmorillonite clay for twenty-eight days. The majority of goats have some level of heavy metal exposure from the soils, rainfall, and the additives in vaccines or feeds. If the goat tests as needing heavy metal detox, I add zeolite mineral (see the Resources page for shopping links). The goat may test for a stronger detox, such as a fourteen-day round of Dynamite Herbal Tonic.

There are many other excellent herbal detox formulas formulated for goats on the market. Several brands are listed in the cross-reference chart. An internet search will locate others. A good herbal detox formula will encourage the liver, kidneys, and bowels to flush toxins while supporting healthy digestion.

Always muscle test or dowse for the detox appropriate to your goat. Always test whether your goat can tolerate the detox you decided on. If you have any doubts, start with the mildest detox and work up to stronger blends over time. When the goats are done with the detox, then I start the rebuilding program.

Sometimes the goats test to skip the detox entirely for Step 2 and move to rebuilding the body first. I start the goats on my basic supplement program of free-choice vitamins and minerals, after testing the goat for the program.

Regardless of which option your goats test to start first, Step 2 is two parts: a detox and the beginning of rebuilding the body. Either can happen first; it depends on the priority for that goat. The combination of detox and rebuilding will take about five months total, which puts Step 3 at about six months. Important: If at any time during Step 2 the goat is surrendering to parasites, test to see if chemicals are needed to save the goat. Parasite symptoms can be confused with detox symptoms, which can include diarrhea, runny nose and/or eyes, skin eruptions, weight loss, and hair loss. Before assuming that a symptom is caused by parasites during this period, I muscle test or dowse. A fever, anemia, yellow or green snot, or bloody diarrhea are likely not effects of the detox, and muscle testing or dowsing may indicate treatment with herbs or conventional medications. If you have any doubts about your muscle testing or dowsing abilities please do not risk your goat. Call the vet.

Step 3, months six through twelve: At this point you have transitioned the feed and hay, gone through a detox, and spent several months rebuilding nutritional reserves with the highest quality supplement program you can find. Four months is the amount of time it takes for the blood to be completely replaced and is often the milestone when major shifts in health occur. Another key milestone is two years. In two years, the body replaces all the bone. This is typically when you'll see your herd reach full health, although it can take longer if the transition was rocky.

Step 3 is continuing the basic optimum nutrition program, and starting to transition your dewormers over. During the first two steps, ideally you have been able to take a break from vaccines and chemicals. Now, as we move into month six, continue to assess. If you suspect parasites are an issue, muscle test or dowse. Start testing for the mildest non-chemical dewormer, such as diatomaceous earth (DE), clay, pumpkin seeds, pine needles, lespedeza, trefoil, chicory, or one of the commercially available herbal blends (I use Dynamite Herbal Tonic). If none of the non-chemical dewormers test as clearing the parasite issue, muscle test or dowse the chemical options. A list of basic chemical options is included

in the section on parasites. After the chemical dewormer, wait forty-eight hours and then do a detox with clay to remove the chemical residue. Clay has a negative charge and will bind with the positively charged deworming chemicals still in the gut and carry them out of the body. Clay works mainly on toxins in the digestive tract. You may choose to muscle test or dowse to see if your goat also needs the chemicals removed from the bloodstream. If so, test zeolite (negative charge *and* small enough to enter the blood stream) or other detox herbs from the cross-reference chart. As the months progress, you should find that you are having to resort to the chemicals less and less often. If you get to the end of the first year, and still need chemicals on a regular basis, you need to revisit your basic nutrition program and your pasture management, and pay special attention to copper and zinc.

Step 4, month thirteen through forty-eight: During months thirteen through forty-eight, continue following all the previous steps. Continue the healthy diet. Continue monitoring mucous membranes and body condition. Continue testing for non-chemical as well as chemical options. You should observe an overall trend of testing for chemicals and medications less and less.

Step 4 is also when you take another look at immunity and vaccines. As your goat becomes healthier you should be seeing illnesses less frequently. There will be times when the goat is under stress, such as when traveling to shows or kidding, that the immune system may need an extra boost. If you anticipate an extra stress on the goat, test for daily prebiotics, some extra vitamin C (preferably as Ester-C with added bioflavonoids or herbal immune boosters (see the cross-reference chart for ideas). The only vaccine currently available for goats is the Caseous lymph-adenitis (CL) vaccine. However, some folks do use the rabies vaccine on their goats as well. Rather than debate whether vaccines are necessary, I will just offer that if you choose to vaccinate, you can place a clay poultice on the vaccination site immediately after removing the needle and start clay and zeolite orally (muscle test or dowse the dosage and frequency) to remove the preservatives and mercury right away. Personally, I give one dose of homeopathic nux vomica 30c immediately to counteract any vaccine side effects (or lyssin 30c if using the rabies vaccine). You may choose to muscle test or dowse for nux vomica also.

If your goat has a history of vaccines, you may want to muscle test or dowse to determine if your goat has vaccinosis. The symptoms of vaccinosis can look like many other diseases and are as varied as behavioral changes, hair loss, or failure to thrive. If testing indicates vaccinosis, then muscle test or dowse these remedies: thuja occidentalis 30c, lyssin 30c, or silicea 30c, including the number of doses.

In Europe, there has been some work done with homeopathic nosodes. Nosodes are homeopathic remedies containing the vibrational signatures of different diseases. Some feel nosodes can be used to encourage to body's immune system to fight off a specific disease. Nosodes exist for CL, caprine arthritis and encephalitis (CAE), and Johne's disease in goats. You must contact an experienced livestock homeopath to administer nosodes. I use these nosodes in my herd to boost immunity against these diseases under veterinary supervision. The nosodes come as tiny sugar pellets, usually given orally in several doses over a period of time. As with homeopathy in general, some debate exists as to their effectiveness. Also, as with all homeopathy in general, the remedies work best in a well-mineralized toxin-free goat. See the Resources page for suggestions on locating a homeopathic livestock veterinarian.

7

Diet Basics

Minerals

Antagony. Synergy. Two words critical to understanding goat nutrition and minerals. All minerals have other minerals that either suppress (antagony) or enhance (synergy) their uptake and use in the body. Additionally, minerals come in multiple chemical forms. The inorganic forms are oxides, sulfates, and carbonates. These are only 1–10 percent absorbable and more difficult for the body to excrete. Inorganic minerals have a tendency to build up in the body, or bioaccumulate, sometimes in odd places. Inorganic minerals also have a larger particle size, above 5,000 daltons.* Minerals must be below 5,000 daltons to be absorbed. At the other end of the absorbability scale are the organic minerals, the amino acid chelates.

Chelation is the process by which a mineral is bonded to an amino acid, which in nature is how plants make the minerals

---

* The Dalton (Da or u) is the standard unit for atomic mass.

they take from the soil usable. Animals also chelate minerals in the body from the foods they eat. Scientists in the 1960s worked to improve the bioavailability of minerals by chelating a metal ion before feeding the mineral to an animal. Chelates are generally above 90 percent absorbable, while minerals in the oxide, sulfate, or carbonate form are typically no more than 10 percent absorbable. As a result, an animal must eat much more of non-chelated minerals in order to meet its needs, and all the surplus minerals it can't absorb have to go somewhere, often turning into deposits in the body or causing toxicity issues.

Albion Minerals was the original patent holder on the chelation process and has lots of research information on their website.* H. DeWayne Ashmead, the current president of Albion and son of founder Harvey H. Ashmead, was the scientist who researched minerals and chelation extensively. You can find his research papers online or read his book *Amino Acid Chelation in Human and Animal Nutrition*. Albion is still a good source of scientific information on chelation, although they have sold the animal portion of the company and focus primarily on human health and nutrition now.

WHAT IS A CHELATE?

A chelate is a mineral element attached to an organic ligand molecule. To be categorized as a chelate the mineral must have two points of attachment on the ligand. There are many possible types of chelates, including some that are toxic. The term "chelate" does not define the ligand type or size, both of which are critical. Size matters because size affects absorption. The combined size of the ligand and mineral should be smaller than the size of the cell absorbing it, or it cannot fit. If the combined size is too large, the bond must be broken, which then makes the mineral unstable and more likely to cause harm or pass entirely out of the body. Amino acid chelates use amino acids for the organic ligand and are small enough to be easily absorbed.

Proteinates, complexes, and other forms fall in between the inorganics and the amino acid chelates for absorption and excretion. Because of the complex relationships between minerals, I suggest being very careful about singling out just one, or even just a couple, to use in supplementing your goat. You can very easily upset the balance and throw something else out of whack, and if the minerals are not easy to excrete, the problem is compounded. Generally speaking, goats do best consuming a blend of amino acid chelates and inorganic minerals. The chelates catalyze the absorption of the inorganics.

---

* www.albionminerals.com

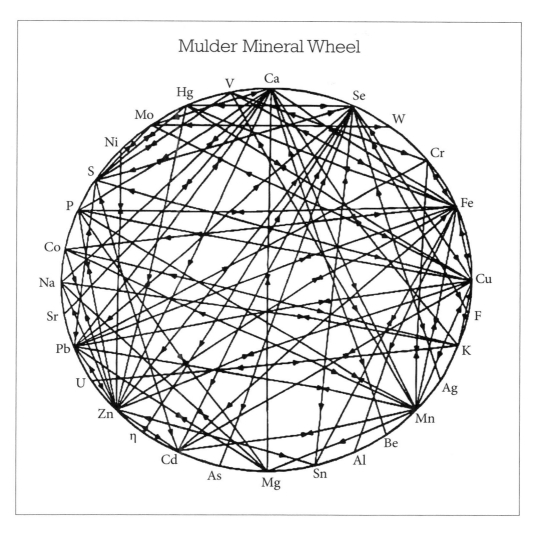

Mulder Mineral Wheel

The Mulder Mineral Wheel depicts the relationships and interactions between trace minerals. Source: David L. Watts, Trace Elements and Other Essential Nutrients (Henderson, NV: Meltdown Intl, 1995), 17.

Herbs or plant-based minerals are another source of more easily absorbed or excreted minerals. I personally still use amino acid chelates rather than plant-based supplements because the minerals in a particular herb or plant as much as the "energy" of that herb contribute to the herb's effectiveness. Mineral and energetic properties can vary widely in the same herb, for three main reasons. First, many herbs are native to certain areas of the globe and get their mineral and energetic properties from their place of origin. Herbs grown away from their original home may or may not be as effective. Second, herbs also depend on healthy soil with sufficient minerals to have full potency. Third, the handling and processing of the herbs will affect potency too. For all these reasons, I consider amino acid chelates to be a more consistent mineral source.* The amino acid chelation process, and only that lab process, produces standardized minerals that are chelated as if they had been through the plant kingdom first, so you know exactly what you are getting. And of course, bottom line: when in doubt, muscle test. Go with what tests well, be it herb or chelated mineral. As holistic physician Dr. Gabriel Cousens said, "Minerals are frequencies of light, frequencies of information, and frequencies of creation for the material world in the universe in which we live. Minerals activate all the catalysts for enzymatic reactions in the body."

Many of the studies determining which minerals are needed by the body in what amounts and ratios, which in turn determine how to balance minerals with rations, are seriously flawed. The studies do not take into account the absorption and excretion rates of minerals in their various forms (i.e., iron as an oxide is a very different material than iron as an amino acid chelate). So many of the "rules" we have been taught about how much to give of each mineral are off-base. The relationships of synergy and antagony are so complex that it is very, very difficult to single out just one mineral in a study and determine an ideal amount. Science has a hard time improving on nature. Nature allows for free-choice access to chelated minerals, so the body can pick and choose and easily excrete any excess. For example, let's look at studies determining copper needs in goats. Did the copper study take into account all the minerals that enhance or inhibit copper uptake? Were those minerals analyzed in every bale of hay and every plant the goats ate? Did the study take into account that darker-skinned goats need up to eight times as much copper as light-skinned goats? Did it take into account variations in age, sex, breed, and size? Finally, did the study take into account the proven phenomenon that simply by observing a study, the observer actually exerts an energetic influence over the outcome?†

To scientifically balance a ration according to a mineral chart we would literally have to individually analyze every bale of hay, even those harvested from the same field. Was it grown on a hill or in a hollow of the same field? The soil composition within a field can be completely different in different areas. What is the weather and barometric pressure at the time the goat is eating? Low pressure systems cause the body to throw off calcium due

---

* These same three factors should be taken into account when choosing essential oils.
† The observer effect, a scientific term stating that merely observing a phenomenon will change it.

to a shift in polarity, so calcium that is balanced for one weather situation will be unbalanced for another. Is the animal pregnant or in estrus? Hormones, enzymes, stress, and many other X factors all enter into absorption and assimilation. The goats' instincts are far more evolved than our intellect.

Importance and Controversy of Copper

There are many minerals important to goat health. I'm singling out copper first because, in my opinion, copper is the most misunderstood and the most underfed of all the minerals goats need. In order to talk about supplementing goats with copper, let's first understand what copper is, as well as some generally accepted principles about copper and goats that can be found in any book on chemistry, physiology, or goat care.

- Copper is a metal element important in many functions in the body.
- Copper can exist in several forms.
- Elemental copper (Cu) is copper all by itself and very reactive.
- Copper compounds are copper bonded to other elements, such as copper sulfate or copper oxide.
- Copper can also bond to protein, making copper proteinate.
- Finally, copper can form a true chelate with amino acids. A true chelate is defined by low molecular weight, one bond ionic and one covalent, and neutralized electrical charge.
- The form of copper ingested is critical. Copper oxides are very hard to absorb and use. Copper sulfates are more absorbable. Copper proteinate is even more absorbable. Copper–amino acid chelate is the most absorbable. Amino acid–chelated copper also catalyzes the uptake of the more unabsorbable forms and is the only form of copper that does not have to be broken apart in the gut into elemental copper (Cu), as was established by the research of H. De-Wayne Ashmead.
- Other minerals can inhibit or enable copper uptake. What you feed with the copper is just as important as the copper itself, and this includes your water, pasture, hay, and grain.
- Iron is a copper inhibitor. If you live in an area of high-iron soils, you are more likely to need additional copper.
- Zinc is closely tied to both copper and iron, as is sulfur. All minerals are connected. Focusing on just one will drive you crazy and leave your goats with either too much or

too little of something. These mineral relationships have been well established in the research community and are commonly portrayed on Mulder's Mineral Wheel.

- Goats need more copper than sheep. Feeding a supplement designed for sheep will lead to copper deficiency and health issues. This is a generally accepted principle found in all goat care manuals and on feed labels.
- Copper has the potential to accumulate in the liver. If the animal is stressed, it can release suddenly, causing a severe health crisis. This is also a generally accepted principle and can be found on product warning labels.

So, having established some of the basics, let's circle back to how copper gets into a goat. First the goat eats something containing copper, including copper boluses.

- If the goat ate elemental copper (Cu), which is very reactive and unlikely to exist without being bonded, then the elemental copper would either react with ingredients in the gut, preventing absorption, or would be absorbed.
- If the goat ate a copper compound (for example copper oxide Cu_2O) or copper proteinate, the copper would split away from whatever it is bonded to in the gut during digestion. This splitting leaves behind elemental copper to react or be absorbed (Cu_2O is split into copper and oxygen).
- If the goat ate amino acid–chelated copper, the copper could be easily absorbed. The copper is not highly reactive and does not have to be split apart.

Remember, elemental copper (Cu) is very reactive. It is just as likely to react with ingredients in the gut as it is to absorb. The only copper stable enough to be absorbed and resist reacting with other items in the gut is amino acid–chelated copper.

Absorption takes place through the mucosa that lines the digestive tract into the blood stream or into the lymph. The lymph and blood carry the minerals and nutrients to the liver, which regulates copper levels in the bloodstream and stores copper reserves for times when copper supply is low.[*] If the liver has more copper than is needed, the extra copper is excreted in the bile and passes out of the body in the feces. The body has the ability to chelate minerals in the liver. This process takes

---

[*] There is some debate about the location of copper storage. Some feel it may be the intestinal wall. The liver is the more commonly accepted location.

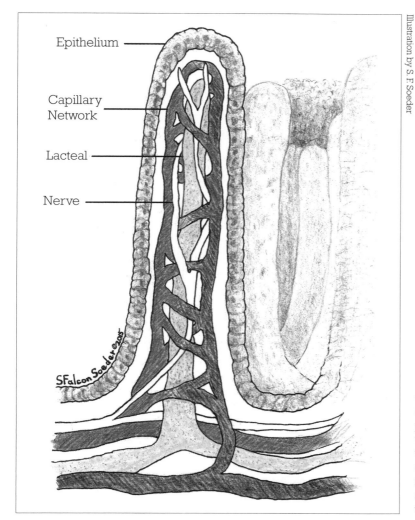

Illustration by S. F. Soeder

Epithelium

Capillary
Network

Lacteal

Nerve

SFalconSoeder@2015

Copper absorption takes place through the mucosa that lines the digestive tract, into the blood stream or into the lymph.

time, energy, and amino acid resources, and it's not always completed for every elemental metal that makes it into the system. The liver also bonds the elemental copper to proteins, mainly ceruloplasmin and albumin. Copper *must* be bonded to a protein by the liver to be used by the body after it is absorbed from the digestive tract.

Remember, elemental copper that isn't bonded is very reactive. Copper that isn't bonded to a protein floats free in the bloodstream. Because it has a positive charge and is reactive, it causes oxidative stress (think internal rust), or it looks for something to bond with and then deposits in unintended locations, especially the brain and reproductive organs. Bonding elemental copper to ceruloplasmin takes energy, requires the correct supply of amino acids, and depends on the reactive elemental making it to the liver without reacting with something it meets along the way. Not all elemental copper will make it to the liver to be bonded to ceruloplasmin.

All copper that makes it into the gut and is absorbed will either be absorbed as an amino acid chelate, highly stable and ready to use, or as a very reactive elemental copper (Cu) molecule. So the form of the copper ingested determines whether or not the copper can be absorbed and how easily it is absorbed. The health of the liver then determines whether the absorbed copper will be used for health or will create toxic issues in the body.

In nature, goats eat copper in a variety of compounds and chelates and generally do just fine. So why do goats get into trouble with copper toxicity? Because goats in nature are not being fed the large quantities of copper compounds that the domestic goats receive in feeds and supplements.

Copper supplementation for goats in the United States is still a topic of much debate and discussion and has been the subject of less research than has the copper needs of sheep, cattle, and horses. In Europe, copper needs for dairy goats have been established.

Salt

Salt is a foundation nutrient for goats, one that is very often misused, underused, overused, or used in ways the goats cannot utilize. So, let's learn about salt.

First, when folks say salt, the mineral that is really being referred to is sodium. Salt itself is sodium chloride (NaCl). Sodium is very reactive and thus never found in nature by itself. When salt is eaten, the body splits the sodium and chloride apart.

Salt is critical for good health. It activates the first digestive enzyme in the mouth, salivary amylase. In the parietal cells of the stomach wall, sodium chloride generates hydrochloric acid, one of the most important of all digestive secretions. Salt is also used to maintain the fluid and mineral balance between the outside and the inside of the cells in the body. Inside the cell, potassium is higher; outside, sodium is higher. The negatively charged potassium anion and positively charged sodium cation create an electrochemical gradient called membrane

If you want to dig deeper into the transmutation debate, look up the work of C. Louis Kervran, Nobel Prize nominee, and the 1990s research of Panos T. Pappas.

potential. Membrane potential is responsible for heart function, nerve impulse transmission, and muscle contraction. There is speculation that blood salt levels drop due to sweating loss as well as transmutation of sodium to potassium. The salt the goats eat restores the blood salt levels and keeps the cells balanced.

This delicate balance between sodium and potassium in the body is the reason that salt should not be force-fed or withheld. Allowing goats to choose how much to consume each day lets them maintain their sodium balance. How much salt is enough salt for a goat? Well, that really depends on the goat, the diet, the current temperature, stress levels, etc. Basically, the goat will eat as much or as little as is necessary for good health. Sometimes that's just a nibble; sometimes it's a very large quantity, ounces per day. Always provide plenty of fresh water as well as salt that is not mixed with other supplements, feed, or additives that could limit or artificially encourage consumption.

Salt is often added to feed and supplement mixes, usually to improve the taste or limit consumption of the minerals. You will often see two different listings on the guaranteed analysis: a sodium Na listing and a salt NaCl listing. This practice is done to account for sodium that may be in the feed as other sodium compounds. The sodium Na listing includes the NaCl. Manufacturers sometimes hide high salt levels by listing the salt multiple times in the ingredient list. Generally speaking, unless the product is a salt supplement, you should not see salt showing up in the top five ingredients.

Salt supplements are available as blocks or loose. Salt comes in white, pink, gray, tan, and other colors. It can be bought plain or with added ingredients.

In my opinion, loose salt rather than block salt is better for goats. Much of the reason for this lies with goats' tongues. Goats' tongues are smooth, like horses'. Cows, on the other hand, have very rough tongues. A cow can lick a salt block and sandpaper off a day's supply of salt. Goats, even more than horses, are unable to get sufficient salt from solid blocks. Failing to lick enough salt off a block, a horse or goat will bite the block to break off chunks. Biting those blocks has the potential to injure the temporomandibular joint, also known as the TMJ, the joint where the jaw connects to the skull. In technical terms, the TMJ is the point where the mandible is tucked underneath the zygomatic arch. The TMJ is the only paired joint in the body and is critical for proper spinal alignment, which in turn affects thousands of nerves located at the first few vertebrae of the neck.

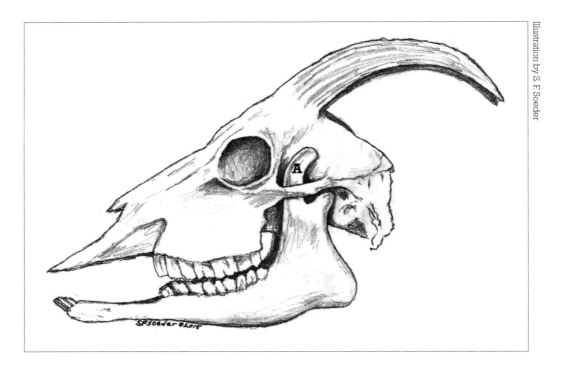

Illustration by S. F. Soeder

The TMJ is the area around point A where the mandible is tucked under the zygomatic arch.

Additionally, many blocks are formed using binding agents. Binding agents are an unnecessary and potentially unhealthy addition to the goats' diet. Some examples of unhealthy binding agents would be waste clay from vegetable oil refining (which contains the impurities removed from the oil), lignin sulfonate (a by-product from the wood pulp industry), or cement (which may contain heavy metals). Blocks often also have flavoring or coloring added. Mineral blocks have minerals added. The minerals are non-chelated and not easily absorbed or excreted. To learn more about chelated and non-chelated minerals, see the section on minerals.

Loose salt allows goats to consume as much salt as needed without stressing the TMJ or adding binding agents to the diet.

Not all loose salts are equal though. First of all, loose salt should clump when the weather is humid. Salt that does not clump has been treated with flow enhancers or anti-caking agents. Common additives are ferrocyanide, yellow prussiate of soda, tricalcium phosphate, aluminum-calcium silicate, and sodium aluminosilicate. Beyond their potential toxicity, these additives prevent salt from mixing with water in the body.

Natural salt is never white. Natural salt colors are tan, gray, or pink. Refined white salt is processed with aluminum (toxic metal), ferrocyanide (toxic), and bleach (forms a dioxin that causes cancer).

Salt is either mined from the ground or made by evaporating sea water. The issue with sea salt is that the oceans have become fairly polluted. Radiation, heavy metals, and industrial pollution are all found in the world's oceans today. Mined salt typically comes from old deposits, laid down before pollution was an issue. That being said, a reputable salt company tests its salt for contaminants and can provide an analysis upon request.

Reading Feed and Supplement Labels

Grain these days is often less palatable because of the mineral deficiencies in the soil. The grain can't hold as much sugar (measured in degrees Brix) when the mineral concentration is low. Low-Brix, low-mineral grain will not taste as good, and most feed companies add flavorings or sweeteners to hide the taste. The feed industry continues to create and adapt new sweeteners. If you don't recognize the name of an ingredient, I encourage you to look it up. A goat's diet is not normally high in sugars, so sweetened feeds are probably best avoided.

Fats should be vegetable based, not petroleum or animal based. Mineral oil is not a substance the body is designed to recognize and digest, and animal fats are for carnivores, not herbivorous goats.

Fats can go rancid and must be preserved. Preservatives can be natural and healthy or chemical and toxic. The three worst preservatives still allowed in feed are butylated hydroxyanisole (BHA), butylated hydroxytoluene (BHT), and ethoxyquin. All are toxic and potentially carcinogenic (cancer causing). It is important to note that, by law, if a feed manufacturer buys fats already preserved prior to purchase, the preservatives do not need to be listed on the feed label. Know and trust your manufacturer!

Mold inhibitors are another common feed additive. Any feed with a moisture content above 13 percent will typically have mold inhibitors added. Acetic acid, propionic acid, and butyric acid are safe. Others are not.

Corn oil is another red flag on the label, as the majority of corn these days is genetically modified (GMO), unless labeled organic. Additionally, corn oil is high in omega-6 fats and may be inflammatory.

Canola oil should also be avoided. Canola is a name invented by the Rapeseed Association in Canada for certain cultivars of rapeseed. Canola oil originally became popular as an industrial machine lubricant during World War II and was too bitter and too acidic for consumption. Canola plants were bred to remove the acids and bitterness so the oil could be used in cooking. However, over 90 percent of the world canola crop is now GMO.

Among the remaining healthy oils, total fat content is still an important factor. A goat's natural diet is not exceptionally high in fat, other than seeds and nuts. Large amounts of oils have the potential to tie up receptor sites for the fat-soluble vitamins A, D, E, and K. If oils are listed among the first few ingredients or the feed is obviously oily, there are likely healthier options.

There is one last monkey wrench in reading labels. The FDA approves lists of ingredients for different classes of feeds and supplements. If an item is not on the list, it cannot be on the label. So what the label says and what is actually in the feed or supplement may appear to be different. Citrus by-product meal may actually be very high-quality citrus bioflavonoid. Filler may actually be DE or clay. Sulfur may be methylsulfonylmethane (MSM). Or the by-product meal, filler, and sulfur may be exactly that—lower-quality ingredients. Another good argument for knowing and trusting the manufacturer and learning to muscle test: You can easily do a liver reflex point test or a push-pull test while in the store shopping.

8

Prebiotics and Gut Health: The Foundation

Both healthy and unhealthy bacteria are always present in the digestive tract of ruminants. Bacteria are able to go dormant when conditions are not right for them to flourish (this is how bacteria evade antibiotics). In a healthy goat, the helpful bacteria are active and multiplying, and the harmful bacteria are in dormancy. A healthy gut needs the correct pH, food for the bacteria to eat, and minimal adrenaline stress. Food for bacteria is the "soup" of plant matter making its way through the gut. The bacteria feed on the soup of chewed-up, partially digested plant matter and actually help break some of it down.

The ideal pH varies depending on the area of the digestive tract. The pH is affected by the food being eaten as well as adjusted by the goat. Lower-protein plant matter leaves behind an alkaline ash residue when digested. Proteins leave behind acid ash. The goat adjusts the pH of the gut contents with the saliva, hydrochloric acid, and bile. Generally speaking, food matter in the rumen, reticulum, and omasum has a healthy pH range of 6.0–6.8. This pH range is maintained by the saliva, which contains alkalizing minerals that buffer pH. Food matter in the abomasum (true stomach) has a pH of 2.5 because of the hydrochloric acid. Food matter leaving the abomasum is buffered to a pH of 7.0–8.0 with alkaline bile from the gallbladder as it moves into the intestines. Helpful bacteria adapted to the correct pH range (and harmful bacteria that thrive outside that range) are present both before the true stomach and in the intestines.

Adrenaline stress is the third factor that affects healthy digestion. A prey animal, such as a goat, must be able to react instantly to perceived danger or risk becoming a meal. The fight-or-flight response is the name given to the physiological response to a perceived threat to survival. When frightened, the animal's hypothalamus activates two systems: the sympathetic nervous system and the adrenal-cortical system. A flood of hormones enters the bloodstream to set the body up for fast action. Two key points to remember are that once these hormones are in the bloodstream, they must be burned off or used up, and one function of the hormones is to shut down digestion. Until enough time passes for those hormones to be out of the bloodstream, digestion will be stopped and food will be fermenting or rotting wherever it happens to be sitting in the digestive tract. This in turn will change the pH and allow the bad bacteria to come out and play.

Antibiotics, Probiotics, and Prebiotics

When the gut grows stressed and gut conditions become less than ideal, the healthy bacteria go dormant and the harmful bacteria begin to outnumber the healthy bacteria. I generally see three tactics used to combat dominant harmful bacteria: antibiotics to kill the harmful bacteria, probiotics to repopulate the gut, and prebiotics to change the gut conditions. Of these three, two are not very effective.

Antibiotics do not work in the way we commonly assume they do. Antibiotics actually drive harmful bacteria into dormancy rather than truly kill them all. Studies have proven that bacteria can go dormant when gut conditions are not favorable, and antibiotics are unable to kill bacteria in a dormant state. When an antibiotic is used, some of the harmful bacteria go dormant and evade the antibiotic. Antibiotics can drive the harmful bacteria back into dormancy, but they cannot prevent

Fight-or-Flight Response

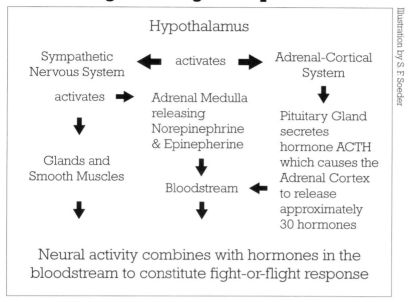

Illustration by S. F. Soeder

Hypothalamus

Sympathetic Nervous System ← activates → Adrenal-Cortical System

activates → Adrenal Medulla releasing Norepinephrine & Epinepherine

Pituitary Gland secretes hormone ACTH which causes the Adrenal Cortex to release approximately 30 hormones

Glands and Smooth Muscles

Bloodstream ←

Neural activity combines with hormones in the bloodstream to constitute fight-or-flight response

them from coming back and can do nothing against new harmful bacteria introduced from outside the body.

Probiotics also have a drawback. Most probiotics work on the theory that the bacteria in the gut need to be repopulated. However, the bacteria are always there, both the healthy bacteria and the nasty ones, so using probiotics on an unhealthy gut will not rebalance the bacterial population of the gut. The healthy bacteria from the probiotic will just go dormant right along with the bacteria already in dormancy. Additionally, there is a very good possibility that probiotics given orally will not survive past the strong acids in the true stomach. Rumen stomachs are especially designed to kill large amounts of bacteria, much more so than a monogastric (one-stomach) animal. Rumen stomachs excrete large amounts of an enzyme that breaks down the bacterial cell walls.

The third approach is using a prebiotic. A good prebiotic is designed to provide the ideal "soup" for the healthy bacteria to live in. It also balances the gut pH and contains ingredients that reduce mental and emotional stress, calm the animal, and relax the muscles. When the gut is restored to ideal conditions, the good bacteria will leave dormancy and begin to repopulate while the harmful bacteria will enter dormancy or die off. Using a good probiotic to boost the healthy rumen bacteria along with the prebiotic can be useful, although it is not necessary. How and when you use your prebiotic is just as important as your choice of prebiotic. Remember, the stress hormones from the fight-or-flight response must be burned off or used up from the bloodstream after they are released. The best time to use a prebiotic is *before* the stress occurs and the body releases hormones, shutting down digestion. If you know you will be rounding up goats, trimming hooves, hauling to a show, or if you have a goat about to kid or any other stress you can control the timing of, give the prebiotic in the feed before the stressor occurs. For stresses you cannot control, the frequency of the dose is as important as the amount. Give small amounts of prebiotic to the stressed animal every few minutes and continue for a couple of hours after the stress occurred. Giving prebiotics as a preventative will keep the helpful bacteria active.

Parasites

Parasites are all about the immune system. A healthy immune system fights off parasites and is stimulated by the presence of a small number of parasites. If the immune system is not the key, then how can you have a field of goats, all exposed to the same parasites, and some show symptoms while others thrive?

I cannot say enough about the importance of copper. Goats must have healthy copper levels to fight off parasites. Copper is especially important for immune function. As stated in chapter 7, because minerals act both synergistically and antagonistically, you also have to look at other minerals that interact with copper. Mulder's chart expresses the relationships visually. Copper can be added to feed, offered free choice, or bolused. I personally prefer free choice so the goat can choose the most appropriate levels. I have used both copper sulfate dissolved in water and dry copper sulfate added to my free-choice mineral mix. Boluses are also very popular among many producers. Some breeders prefer to bolus smaller doses several times a year to keep the copper levels more consistent.[*] I continue to experiment with the best approach to copper for my herd. In general, I feel the research supports that chelated minerals are safer because the excess is easier to excrete. That being said, copper sulfate has years of use

---

[*] Here is an excellent article about copper boluses: R Fainting Farm, "Copper Supplement: Why Supplement Copper?," *Goat Spots*, http://rfaintingfarm.com/copper.html (accessed December 2014).

behind it as a free-choice option for goats and other livestock. Each producer has to watch his herd and make his own informed decisions about copper. If parasites are a problem, the coat looks bleached out, the hair is fishhooked at the end, or the goat's tail looks like a fishtail, the goat may be suffering from a copper deficiency. In general, animals with black skin may need up to eight times more copper than animals with pink skin.

Parasites go through stages of activity that are linked to the moon phases and the time of day. Fecal tests should be done at the same moon stage and same time of day for consistent results. Deworming at the full moon is the most effective, when cell fluid pressure is at peak. If I am doing a three- or seven-day deworming, I make sure the full moon falls at the middle of the process. Rather than deworming by the calendar, deworm as the goats show signs of parasite overload, or if a fecal test reveals a high fecal count.

Dewormers in order of least to most toxic:
1. Montmorillonite/bentonite clay; food-grade diatomaceous earth (DE)
2. Herbal dewormers
3. Chemical dewormers*
    • piperazine, thiabendazole, oxfendazole
    • fenbendazole
    • pyrantel
    • Anthelcide (oxibendazole)
    • ivermectin
    • moxidectin (moxidectin has a very narrow margin of error and should not be used on overweight or underweight animals)

Montmorillonite/bentonite clay has a long history of being used for detoxification and parasite removal. Additionally, this clay is on the FDA Generally Recognized as Safe (GRAS) list. The clay, when wet, carries a strong negative charge (paramagnetic), which attracts positively charged toxins and repels parasites (parasites are diamagnetic). Parasites cannot become resistant to clay.

Food-grade diatomaceous earth works mechanically, by scraping the parasite exoskeleton, causing the parasite to dehydrate and die. While there is debate whether DE is effective on internal goat parasites, most agree that DE is helpful as feed-through

---

* In order by reported deaths in any species, with no deaths for piperazine/thiabendazole/oxfendazole and the most deaths for moxidectin.

fly control and also externally. For large goat operations, the DE can be milled into the grain or fed free choice. DE can be safely fed year round. Always use food-grade DE, which is also recognized by the FDA as having GRAS status. Parasites cannot develop resistance to DE because the action is mechanical. Goats should not breathe in DE dust, so the DE should be dampened with water or otherwise kept from becoming dusty. In spite of the debate over its effectiveness, I include DE in my own herd's parasite program because it muscle tests well for them.

Herbal remedies are an entire book by themselves. There are many brands and herbal combinations using garlic, wormwood, walnut, and other herbs. In general herbal dewormers should be given as needed, rather than by the calendar, as parasites can develop resistance to herbs also. Using combinations of herbs reduces the risk that parasites will develop resistance. Some herbs are not safe during pregnancy, so use professionally prepared mixes or consult with a professional herbalist.

Many folks find that pumpkin seeds are effective against parasites. Acorns, certain types of pine, garlic, cloves, organic black oil sunflower seeds (BOSS), and lespedeza are all mentioned as being effective against parasites.

With a heavily parasitized goat, start mild and work your way up. Bringing out the big guns too early can lead to a massive parasite die-off, which can release toxins capable of killing the goat.

Support the gut after a chemical deworming. Feed a good pre-/probiotic that balances gut pH and encourages healthy gut flora. Also consider adding zeolites and/or montmorillonite clay to the diet for several days, starting twenty-four hours after the chemical dose, to absorb any residual chemical.

Work on clearing parasites from the soil. Clean up manure, if possible, and compost. Try using free-range chickens to eat parasites and break up manure to let the eggs dry out. In small areas, spread diatomaceous earth to kill parasites. Rotate pastures and alternate between browsing and grazing species to break up the parasite life cycle. Feeding the goats from feeders and hay racks rather than on the ground makes a big difference in parasite exposure also.

Cross-Reference Chart of Health Conditions and Potential Solutions

First, and most importantly, *always* test the broad-spectrum basic foundation products first before testing targeted specialty items. Broad-spectrum basics means Dynamite V/M Salt Mix for Browsers and Grazers; Dynamite 2:1, 1:1, and Izmine free-choice products; Vitalerbs available from Fir Meadow or Land of Havilah; Better Daze from Fir Meadow; or your favorite vitamin/mineral blend for your herd. The body requires a healthy foundation to heal illness, so build that foundation first. In many instances, the specific issue will resolve itself within 120 days just by building the foundation of health.

If the foundation support does not address your goat's issue, this chart includes products from four popular goat supplement companies. There are many other remedies and supplements beyond the listings in this chart. The Dynamite product line is specifically listed because I believe Dynamite offers the best mineral products on the market. The Land of Havilah, Fir Meadow, and Molly's Herbs are included because they are among the top three most popular herbal companies for goats. Many readers will find it easier to search for their favorite brand of herbal blends rather than the raw ingredients. You can use the same principles of testing to work your way through product catalogs or lists for your preferred company.

Please be careful singling out a single mineral to increase or reduce. Mineral relationships are a tricky balance of synergy (enhancing each other) and antagony (inhibiting each other). Tweak one mineral and it will affect many others. Start with a professionally formulated blend, either plant-based or amino acid–chelated if possible, and only work with single minerals if muscle testing/dowsing/reflex points indicate, and only in consultation with a medical professional. Some minerals can kill.

If your goat's issue or illness is not included in the chart, please do two things. First, contact me with your suggested edit.* Second, look for the issue or illness most closely related. For example, if your illness is bacterial, see other bacterial illnesses in the chart.

Keep your mind and heart open to additional possible solutions beyond what are listed in the chart here. Ask using muscle testing or dowsing, "Is there a product I should test for this issue beyond what is listed?"

Remember: This chart is for educational purposes. No content in this book is intended to diagnose, treat, or prescribe. Always consult a medical professional. None of the ingredients listed in the chart are being claimed as a cure or treatment for the condition listed.

Oral means take by mouth and swallow it down. So if an issue is in the mouth, and a suggested item says "oral," it means swallow it rather than apply it. Topical means apply on the skin, not internally. Rectal means give via enema or suppository. Vaginal means give via douche or insert vaginally. Dosage, potency, and timing vary too much to even list suggestions. Muscle test for all of these, and *always* consult your medical practitioner before giving anything. Many drugs, herbs, and supplements can interact, sometimes in harmful ways. I cannot stress this enough—consult with a trained professional.

---

* energeticgoat@carrieeastman.com

Photo by Stacy Neely

Beyond the chart of health issues, you may also want to use energy testing to evaluate and custom design other aspects of your goat management program. Use a simple push-pull test or a pendulum to ask questions with yes/no answers. You can test:

- Equipment
- Feed quality
- Hay quality
- Mineral deficiencies
- Supplement quality
- Water quality
- The best color to paint your shelters and kidding stalls
- The best color for collars, halters, and leads

What If My Favorite Herb, Supplement, or Other Item Isn't Listed in the Chart?

Very possibly your favorite will not be listed. There are far too many good-quality supplements and remedies to include in one chart. Simply work from your own list, the product list in your favorite catalog, or a sample of the item you are testing.

Cross-Reference Chart of Health Conditions and Potential Solutions

Challenge	Dynamite	Land of Havilah Herbals	Fir Meadow LLC	Molly's Herbals
READ BEFORE TESTING	Always test DynaPro for every condition. Suggestions assume access to 1 to 1, 2 to 1, Izmine, and salt. Suggestions assume the goat is getting at least one of these as well: V/M Mix for Browsers, V/M Mix for Horses, Dynamite for Horses, or Exotics Plus		For any condition, test for Quantum Touch Energy Medicine	
General Supplements for Basic Vitamin/ Mineral Support	V/M Mix for Browsers and Grazers, 1 to 1, 2 to 1, Izmine, NTM Salt, V/M Salt Mix, Regular Dynamite, V/M Mix for Horses, Exotics Plus	Vitalerbs, Thorvin Kelp, Jurassic Green Powder Cleansing Supplements: Lower Bowel Formula, Kidney Formula, Liver and Gallbladder Formula, Blood Stream Formula	Fir Meadow Organic Kelp; Herb Mixes: Better Daze, God's Greens, Vitalerbs, Kop-Sel, Moringa Powder	Herbal Dietary Supplement, Booster Tonic
Abcesses, Hoof or External	Miracle Clay, Release	X-Ceptic Extract, Complete Tissue & Bone Ointment	HerBiotic Salve, Udder Blast Infusion, Wounderful! Salve, Nav-All Tincture, Oil of Oregano, Super Immune Garlic Extract, Complete Tissue & Bone Ointment, Better Daze Herb Mix, Moringa Powder	Immune ST, Ow-Eze
Abcesses, Internal	Super Stress, Ester-C,★ Hiscorbadyne, Solace, Trace Minerals Concentrate, Miracle Clay (oral)	X-Ceptic Extract, Complete Tissue & Bone Ointment	HerBiotic Extract, Herb Mix, and Salve; MMune Herb Mix; Oil of Oregano; ReBuilld Herb Mix; Super Immune Garlic Extract; Complete Tissue & Bone Capsules or Ointment; Wounderful! Salve; Moringa Powder	

★Ester-C is a registered trademark of the Ester-C Company.

Condition				
Abcesses, Tooth	Trace Minerals Concentrate (topical and/or oral), Super Stress (oral), SOD (oral)	X-Ceptic Extract, Herbal Tooth & Gum Powder, Complete Tissue & Bone Ointment	HerBiotic Salve; see also Internal Abcesses	Molly's Marvelous Salve
Abortion	Breeder Pac, Easy Boy, Solace, Trace Minerals Concentrate	False Unicorn & Lobelia capsules, Female Re-productive Formula, Hormonal Changease Formula, Wheat Germ Oil, Vitalerbs	KeepHer Herb Mix, Wheat Germ Capsules, Bal-Nce, Raspberry Tea Leaves, Moringa Powder, Better Daze, Hormonal Changease Formula, Female Reproductive Formula	Immune ST, Ow-Eze, Preg Tonic
Allergies	Hiscorbadyne, Super Stress, SOD, Ester-C, Yucca, Herbal Tonic, Excel, Dyna Pro, Miracle Clay	Sinus Plus, Lung & Bronchial, ImmuCalm, Liver/Gallbladder, Vitalerbs	Al R G, Fresh Start Herb Mix, Breathe Tea, Lung Support Tincture, Sinus Plus, Chest Formula, Immucalm, Lung & Bronchial, MMunEaze, Better Daze Herb Mix, Moringa Powder, Fresh Start Herb Mix, Vitalerbs	Herbal Dietary Supplement, Booster Tonic, Breathe EZ-T
Anemia	Trace Minerals Concentrate, Dynamite for Horses	Vitalerbs, Jurassic Green	God's Greens Herb Mix, Better Daze Herb Mix, Vitalerbs, Fir Meadow Organic Kelp, Moringa Powder	Herbal Dietary Supplement, Booster Tonic
Anxiety	Tranquil, Relax, Easy Boy	See Stress	See Stress	
Arthritis	Yucca, Ester-C, Hiscorbadyne, SOD, Free & Easy, Herbal Green, MSM, Super Stress	Joint Formula, Complete Tissue & Bone Formula	A-King Joint Support Herb Mix, Wounderful! Salve, ReBuilld Salve, DCongest Salve, Better Daze Herb Mix, Complete Tissue and Bone Formula, Joint Formula, Sen-Sei Ointment, Moringa Powder	Arthritis & Joint Support, Ow-Eze, Aches N' Painz Salve

Challenge	Dynamite	Land of Havilah Herbals	Fir Meadow LLC	Molly's Herbals
Back/Spine Injuries	Izmine, see also Fractures and Nerve Damage	Complete Tissue & Bone Formula (ointment/massage oil & powder/capsule), Vitalerbs	ReBuilld Herb Mix & Salve, Wounderful! Salve, Better Daze Herb Mix, Vitalerbs, Moringa Powder, Complete Tissue and Bone Formula, Sen-Sei Ointment	Ow-Eze, Aches N' Painz Salve
Bacterial Infections	Solace, Ester-C, Hiscorbadyne, Trace Minerals Concentrate, SOD, Super Stress	Infection Formula (not for equine/camelids)	HerBiotic Herb Mix or Salve or Extract, Wounderful! Salve, Udder Blast (external use only), Oil of Oregano, MMune Herb Mix, Fir Meadow Cayenne, Better Daze Herb Mix, Infection Formula (not for camelids/equine), Moringa Powder	Immune ST, Booster Tonic
Birthing Support	Dyna Spark, Dyna Pro	Birth-Prep Formula	Ewe–Ter-N Herb Mix, Birth Prep Formula, Red Raspberry Leaf	Preg Tonic, Mo'Milk
Bloat	Dyna Pro, Miracle Clay	See Colic	Fir Meadow Peppermint Essential oil; see also Colic	
Blood Toxicity	Miracle Clay, Izmine, Herbal Tonic, Excel	Blood Stream Formula	Blood and Cell Support Herb Mix, Cel-lebration Cell Support Mix, Blood Stream Formula, Better Daze Herb Mix, DTox Herb Mix, DVenom Tincture, Moringa Powder	Booster Tonic
Botulism	Miracle Clay, Dyna Pro, Trace Minerals Concentrate	Infection Formula, X-Ceptic Extract	HerBiotic Herb Mix or Extract, MMune Herb Mix, Oil of Oregano, Super Garlic Immune Formula, Infection Formula (not for camelids/equine), Fir Meadow Cayenne, Fresh Garlic Clove(s), Better Daze Herb Mix, Vitalerbs, Moringa Powder	

Brain Function	Izmine, Dyna Pro, Dyna Spark	Memory Plus Formula, Ear & Nerve Extract, Relax-eze Formula, Vitalerbs	Better Brain Blend Herb Mix, Better Daze Herb Mix, Fir Meadow Organic Kelp, Mel O Herb Mix, Relax-Eze Formula, Moringa Powder, Ear & Nerve Support Herb Mix, Memory Plus Formula, MindTrac Formula, Vitalerbs	Immune ST
Burns, First-, Second-, and Third-Degree	Solace (topical), Wound Salve	Comfrey Ointment, Complete Tissue & Bone Formula	Wounderful! Salve, Complete Tissue & Bone Ointment, ReBuilld Herb Mix, God's Greens, Better Daze, Pure Aloe, Complete Tissue & Bone Formula, Moringa Powder	Ow-Eze, Molly's Marvelous Salve
Caprine Arthritis Encephalitis (CAE) Virus	Solace, Trace Minerals Concentrate, see also Arthritis	Infection Formula, Fresh Olive Leaf Tincture, Joint Formula, Vitalerbs, Brigham Tea, and Pumpkin Seed	HerBiotic Herb Mix or Extract, Better Daze Herb Mix, God's Greens, MMune Herb Mix, Fir Meadow Organic Kelp, A-King Joint Support Herb Mix, Lung Tincture, Breathe Tea, Super Immune Garlic Extract, Infection Formula (not for camelids/equine), Oil of Oregano, Fresh Garlic Clove(s), Kop-Sel Herb Mix	Immune ST, Ow-Eze, Booster Tonic, Aches N' Painz Salve
Caseous Lymph-adenitis/Pseudotu-berculosis (Bacteria)	Trace Minerals Concentrate, Solace, SOD, Super Stress, Dyna Pro	Vitalerbs, Brigham Tea, Pumpkin Seed, Mullein & Lobelia Formula, the cleansing formulas	Kop-Sel Herb Mix, Better Daze Herb Mix, Vitalerbs, HerBiotic Herb Mix, ReBuilld Herb Mix, Mmune Herb Mix, Fir Meadow Cayenne, Fresh Start, Blood & Cell Support Herb Mix, Celebration Cell Support Mix, Super Garlic Immune Formula, Mullein Herb Powder, Lobelia Inflata Herb Powder, Moringa Powder	Herbal Dietary Supplement, Herbal Worm Formula

Challenge	Dynamite	Land of Havilah Herbals	Fir Meadow LLC	Molly's Herbals
Cell/Skin Support	Wound Salve, Balm, Release (topical)	Lower Bowel Formula, Kidney Formula, Liver/Gallbladder Formula, Blood Stream Formula, Vitalerbs, Complete Tissue & Bone Formula (powder/capsule, and ointment/massage oil)	Cellebration Cell Support Herb Mix, Cellebration Skin Salve, Better Bowels Herb Mix, Lower Bowel Formula, Fresh Start Herb Mix, Kidney Formula, Blood and Cell Support Herb Mix, Blood Stream Formula, Wounderful! Salve, Complete Tissue and Bone Formula, BFC Shampoo, BFC Soap, Better Daze Herb Mix, Vitalerbs, Moringa Powder	Immune ST
Coccidia	DynaPro, Trace Minerals Concentrate, Herbal Tonic, Miracle Clay	Land of Havilah Parasite Formula	GI Soother Herb Mix, Fir Meadow Cayenne, Better Daze Herb Mix, Fir Meadow Organic Kelp, Garlic Clove(s), Slippery Elm Bark Powder	Immune ST, Herbal Worm Formula, Slippery Elm Bark
Colic, Bloat	Dyna Pro, Relax (oral), Miracle Clay	Liver and Gallbladder Formula, Peppermint Tea (oral), Peppermint Essential Oil and Olive Oil (external), Infection Formula, Soothing Digestion Formula, Activated Charcoal	Colic & Bloat Support Herb Mix, Fir Meadow Peppermint (dilute with olive oil externally onto stomach/rumen area), Better Daze Herb Mix, Fresh Start Herb Mix, Super Garlic Immune Formula, Blood and Cell Support Herb Mix, GI Soother Herb Mix	
Constipation	Easy Boy, Izmine, Dyna Pro		Better Bowels Herb Mix, Lower Bowel Formula, Fir Meadow Cayenne, Fresh Start Herb Mix, Olive Oil	Slippery Elm Bark

Condition				
Copper Deficiency and Toxicity	SOD (deficiency only), Miracle Clay (toxicity only)	Vitalerbs, Brigham Tea, Pumpkin Seed, the cleansing formulas	Kop-Sel Herb Mix, Better Daze Herb Mix, Vitalerbs, Fresh Start Herb Mix, Liver and Gallbladder Formula, Blood and Cell Support Formula, Cellebration Cell Support Formula, DVenom Tincture	
Cuts, Scrapes	Wound Salve, Balm, Solace, Tea Tree Oil, Release (topical)	Complete Tissue & Bone Formula (ointment/ massage oil and powder/ capsule), Vitalerbs	Wounderful! Salve, ReBuild Salve, Herb Mix, Complete Tissue and Bone Formula, HerBiotic Salve, HerBamine Tincture, Better Daze Herb Mix, Vitalerbs, Fir Meadow Lavender Essential Oil	Slippery Elm Bark
Diarrhea— GI Source	Dyna Pro, Herbal Tonic, SOD, Excel, Miracle Clay	Land of Havilah Parasite Formula, Lower Bowel Formula	GI Soother Herb Mix, Slippery Elm Bark Powder, Better Bowels Herb Mix, Lower Bowel Formula, DWorm A Herb Mix	Slippery Elm Bark
Diarrhea— Liver Source	Dyna Pro, Herbal Tonic, SOD, Excel, Miracle Clay	Liver/Gallbladder Formula	Fresh Start Herb Mix, Better Daze Herb Mix, DWorm A Herb Mix, Vitalerbs, Slippery Elm Bark Powder	
Ear Cleaning	Diluted Tea Tree Oil, Balm, Trace Minerals Concentrate	Ear & Nerve Formula extract, Oil of Garlic	Warmed olive oil with HerBiotic extract	Garlic/ Mullein Oil
Ear Infection	Trace Minerals Concentrate (topical/oral), Solace (topical/oral)	Ear & Nerve Formula extract, Oil of Garlic	HerBiotic Extract, Mmune Herb Mix, Better Daze Herb Mix, Vitalerbs, Ear and Nerve Formula Extract, Moringa Powder, Oil of Oregano (external use only).	Garlic/ Mullein Oil
Enterotox-emia	Dyna Pro, Solace, Trace Minerals Concentrate, Miracle Clay	Liver and Gallbladder Formula, Soothing Digestion Formula	ClostridEaze Herb Mix, Fresh Start Herb Mix, Bladder Formula, GI Soother Herb Mix, HerBiotic Herb Mix, Fir Meadow Cayenne, Better Daze Herb Mix, Vitalerbs, Blood and Cell Support Formula, Cellebration Cell Support Formula, DTox Herb Mix, DVenom Tincture, Moringa Powder	

Challenge	Dynamite	Land of Havilah Herbals	Fir Meadow LLC	Molly's Herbals
Eye Conditions, Vision	Breeder Pac	Herbal Eyebright Formula (extract and capsules), Vitalerbs	Eye See Herb Mix, Eye See Salve, Herbal Eyebright Formula, Better Daze Herb Mix, Vitalerbs, God's Greens, Moringa Powder	Booster Tonic, Immune ST, Herbal Worm Formula
Failure to Thrive	Dyna Pro, Excel, Trace Minerals Concentrate, Izmine, Dyna Spark	Vitalerbs, Land of Havilah Parasite Formula	Better Daze Herb Mix, GI Soother Herb Mix, DWorm A Herb Mix	Shoo-Fly Spray Mix
Flies	Dyna Shield, Miracle Clay, Balm	Quit Buggin' Essential Oil Blend	Fir Meadow Eucalyptus, Lavender Essential Oil (diluted)	Arthritis & Joint Support
Founder	Easy Balance, Dyna Pro, Super Stress, MSM, topical Release, Breeder Pac, Herbal Green	Vitalerbs, Complete Tissue & Bone Formula (ointment/massage oil, and powder/capsules)	A-King Joint Support, Wounderful! Salve, ReBuilld Herb Mix, Better Daze Herb Mix, Vitalerbs, God's Greens, Fir Meadow Organic Kelp, Moringa Powder, Complete Tissue & Bone Formula	Ow-Eze, Molly's Marvelous Salve, Aches N' Painz Salve
Fractures	Izmine, 1 to 1, 2 to 1, Release (topical)		Wounderful! Salve, ReBuilld Herb Mix, HerBamine Tincture, Complete Tissue & Bone Formula, Vitalerbs, Moringa Powder, God's Greens, Fir Meadow Organic Kelp	Immune ST, Molly's Marvelous Salve
Fungal Infections	Tea Tree Oil, Balm, Solace (topical)	Vitalerbs, Complete Tissue & Bone Formula (ointment/massage oil, and powder/capsules)	HerBiotic Herb Mix or Salve or Extract, Better Daze Herb Mix, Vitalerbs, MMune Herb Mix, Lavender Essential Oil, Tea Tree Essential Oil (diluted), DYeast Herb Mix, Oil of Oregano, Vitalerbs, Super Garlic Immune Formula, Infection Formula Extract (not for camelids/equine)	Immune ST

Condition				
Goat Polio	Solace, Trace Minerals Concentrate, Dyna Pro, Easy Boy	Vitalerbs, Spirulina Extract/Tincture, Infection Formula Extract	Fir Meadow Cayenne, HerBiotic Extract or Herb Mix, Better Daze Herb Mix, Vitalerbs, Super Garlic Immune Formula, Infection Formula (not for camelids/equine), Fir Meadow Rosemary Essential Oil (diluted) for brainstem, DCongest Salve rubbed on brainstem.	
Hearing Support	Izmine	Ear & Nerve Formula extract, Nerve Formula, the cleansing formulas, Vitalerbs	NervEaze Herb Mix, Ear & Nerve Formula, Fresh Start Herb Mix, HerBiotic Herb Mix, Better Daze Herb Mix, Moringa Powder, Vitalerbs	
Heart Support	Hiscorbadyne, Easy Boy, Ester-C, Trace Minerals Concentrate, Izmine	Hawthorn Berry Heart Syrup, Blood Circulation Formula, Vitalerbs	Heart Support Tincture, Better Daze Herb Mix, Vitalerbs, Fir Meadow Cayenne, Blood Circulation Formula	Immune ST, Booster Tonic, Molly's Marvelous Salve
Hoof Rot	Excel, Miracle Clay (oral), Tea Tree Oil, Solace	X-Ceptic Extract, Complete Tissue & Bone (ointment and/or powder/capsules)	HerBiotic Salve or Herb Mix, Nav-All Tincture, Udder Blast Infusion, Wounderful! Salve, ReBuilld Salve, Oil of Oregano, Fresh Start Herb Mix, Better Daze Herb Mix, Vitalerbs, Moringa Powder, DWorm A Herb Mix, Super Garlic Immune Formula, Complete Bone & Tissue Formula	Ow-Eze, Aches N' Painz Salve
Inflammation, Swelling	Yucca, Release (topical), Ester-C, Hiscorbadyne, MSM	Complete Tissue & Bone Formula (ointment/massage oil and powder/capsule), Vitalerbs	HerBamine Tincture, A-King Joint Support, DCongest Salve, Better Daze Herb Mix, Vitalerbs, Wounderful! Salve, Complete Tissue & Bone Formula	Ow-Eze, Molly's Marvelous Salve, Aches N' Painz Salve

Challenge	Dynamite	Land of Havilah Herbals	Fir Meadow LLC	Molly's Herbals
Insect Repellant	Dyna Shield	Quit Buggin' Essential Oil Blend	Fir Meadow Essential Oils: Citronella, Lavender, Peppermint, Eucalyptus	Shoo-Fly Spray Mix, Molly's Mosquito Mix
Johne's Disease	Trace Minerals Concentrate, Solace, Dyna Pro	Soothing Digestion, Infection Formula, Vitalerbs, the cleansing formulas	HerBiotic Herb Mix, Better Daze Herb Mix, Vitalerbs, GI Soother Herb Mix, Mmune Herb Mix, Super Garlic Immune Formula, Fresh Start Herb Mix, Blood & Cell Support Herb Mix, Cellebration Cell Support Herb Mix, DTox Herb Mix, Fir Meadow Organic Kelp, Moringa Powder, Fir Meadow Cayenne	Arthritis & Joint Support, Ow-Eze, Aches N' Painz Salve
Joint Issues	SOD, Ester-C, Hiscorbadyne, Super Stress, SOD, Free & Easy, MSM, Yucca, see also Arthritis	Complete Tissue & Bone Formula (ointment/massage oil & powder/capsule), Joint Formula, Vitalerbs	Wounderful! Salve, A-King Joint Support, DCongest Salve, HerBamine Tincture, Complete Tissue & Bone Formula, Better Daze Herb Mix, Moringa Powder, Vitalerbs	Immune ST, Booster Tonic
Ketosis	Dyna Spark, Herbal Green, Easy Balance	Vitalerbs, Extra Virgin Olive Oil, Raw Honey, Spirulina	ClostridEaze Herb Mix, GI Soother Herb Mix, Fresh Start Herb Mix, Better Daze Herb Mix, Fir Meadow Cayenne, Vitalerbs	
Kidney Support	Herbal Green	Kidney Formula	Kidney, Bladder & Stones Tincture or Herb Mix; DVenom Tincture; Better Daze Herb Mix; Vitalerbs	E Z P
Lactation Support	(covered by foundation program)	Lactation Formula	MilkMaid Herb Mix, God's Greens, Better Daze Herb Mix, Fir Meadow Organic Kelp, Complete Tissue & Bone Formula, Moringa Powder	Mo'Milk

Lice	Dyna Shield	Land of Havilah Parasite Formula; Eucalyptus; Tea Tree, Rosemary, and Lavender Essential Oil in a base of olive oil; the cleansing formulas; Vitalerbs	Fresh Start Herb Mix, Blood & Cell Support Herb Mix, Blood Stream Formula, Wounderful! Salve, DWorm A Herb Mix, Better Daze Herb Mix, Vitalerbs; Fir Meadow Essential Oils (diluted): Eucalyptus, Peppermint, Lavender, Rosemary	
Listeriosis (Bacterial)	Yucca, Trace Minerals Concentrate, Solace, SOD, Super Stress, Hiscorbadyne	Cayenne Extract, Spirulina Extract, Infection Formula, X-Ceptic Extract, Nerve Formula, Relax-eze Formula, Blood Circulation Formula	Fir Meadow Cayenne, HerBiotic Extract, Better Brain Blend Herb Mix, Mel O Herb Mix, Nerve Support Herb Mix, Better Daze, Vitalerbs, Moringa Powder, Super Garlic Immune Formula, Blood Circulation Formula, Relax-Eze Formula	
Liver Flukes	Herbal Tonic, SOD	Land of Havilah Parasite Formula, Liver and Gallbladder Formula	DWorm MLL Tincture, DWorm A Herb Mix, Fresh Start Herb Mix, Better Daze Herb Mix, Moringa Powder, Vitalerbs, Garlic Clove(s)	Herbal Worm Formula
Liver Support	Herbal Tonic, Miracle Clay, Excel	Liver and Gallbladder Formula	Fresh Start Herb Mix, Better Daze Herb Mix, DWorm A Herb Mix, Vitalerbs	
Lung Support	Herbal Green, Super Stress, SOD, Hiscorbadyne, Ester-C	Lung & Bronchial Formula	Breathe Tea (dry coughs), Lung Support Tincture, HerBamine Tincture, DCongest Salve, Herbiotic Herb Mix, Better Daze Herb Mix, Vitalerbs	Breathe EZ-T
Lung Worm	Herbal Tonic, SOD	Land of Havilah Parasite Formula	DWorm MLL Tincture, Garlic Clove(s), Better Daze Herb Mix, Vitalerbs, Fresh Start Herb Mix, Breathe Tea, Lung Support Tincture, Super Garlic Immune Formula	Herbal Worm Formula

Challenge	Dynamite	Land of Havilah Herbals	Fir Meadow LLC	Molly's Herbals
Mange, All Types	Herbal Tonic, Trace Minerals Concentrate, SOD	See Lice	DWorm A Herb Mix, HerBiotic Salve, Wounderful! Salve, Better Daze Herb Mix, Mmune Herb Mix, Fresh Start Herb Mix, Better Daze Herb Mix, Vitalerbs, Moringa Powder	Herbal Worm Formula
Mastitis	Release topical, Solace, Trace Minerals Concentrate, Excel, Ester-C, Hiscorbadyne, SOD	Mullein & Lobelia (fomentation), Glandular Ointment, Complete Tissue & Bone (ointment/massage oil, and powder/capsules), X-Ceptic Formula, Infection Formula	Udder Blast Infusion, MammarEaze Salve, Wounderful! Salve, DCongest Salve, GlandAide Salve, HerBiotic, HerBamine Tincture, Glandular Ointment, Complete Tissue & Bone Formula, Super Garlic Immune Formula, Infection Formula	Immune ST, Mastitis/ Udder Massage Salve
Meningeal Worm	Herbal Tonic, SOD, Yucca, MSM	Land of Havilah Parasite Formula, Nerve Formula, Relax-Eze Formula, Anti-Spasmodic Extract	DWorm MLL Tincture, DWorm A Herb Mix, NerveEaze Salve, Better Brain Blend Herb Mix, Better Daze Herb Mix, Vitalerbs	Herbal Worm Formula
Milk Fever (Hypocalcemia)	Easy Boy, 2 to 1 (topdressed)	Vitalerbs, Extra Virgin Olive Oil, Raw Honey, Spirulina	God's Greens, Fir Meadow Cayenne, Better Daze Herb Mix, Vitalerbs, Moringa Powder	
Milk Production	(addressed by foundation program)	Lactation Formula	MilkMaid, Better Daze Herb Mix, God's Greens, Fir Meadow Organic Kelp, Vitalerbs, ReBuilld Herb Mix	Mo'Milk
Nerve Damage, Support	MSM, OxE Mega, Release (topical)	Nerve Formula, Relax-eze Formula, Complete Tissue & Bone Formula	Better Brain Blend Herb Mix, NervEaze Salve, Nerve Support Herb Mix, Better Daze Herb Mix, Vitalerbs, Wounderful! Salve, ReBuilld Herb Mix or Salve, Complete Tissue & Bone Formula, Relax-Eze	

Condition				
Overeating Disease (Enterotox-emia)	Solace, Trace Minerals Concentrate, Excel, Miracle Clay, Izmine (topdressed)	See Enterotoxemia	See Enterotoxemia	
Pain	Release (topical), MSM, Yucca, Ester-C, Hiscorbadyne, Miracle Clay (topical)	Stop-Ache Formula, Mullein & Lobelia Tincture	HerBamine Tincture, DCongest Salve, Wounderful! Salve, ReBuilld Salve, Sen Sei Balm	Ow-Eze, Aches N' Painz Salve
Parasites—Barberpole	Herbal Tonic, Excel, Miracle Clay, SOD	Land of Havilah Parasite Formula	GI Soother Herb Mix, Slippery Elm Bark Powder, Better Bowels, Lower Bowel Formula, DWorm A Herb Mix, Moringa, Better Daze Herb Mix, Vitalerbs	Herbal Worm Formula
Parasites—Coccidia	Herbal Tonic, Excel, Miracle Clay, Trace Minerals Concentrate, Solace, SOD	Land of Havilah Parasite Formula	GI Soother Herb Mix, Better Daze Herb Mix, Vitalerbs	Herbal Worm Formula
Parasites—External	Dyna Shield, Herbal Tonic, SOD	See Lice	DWorm A, Herbiotic Salve, Wounderful! Salve, Fresh Start Herb Mix, Complete Tissue & Bone Formula	Herbal Worm Formula
Parasites—Giardia	Herbal Tonic, Excel, Miracle Clay, SOD, Trace Minerals Concentrate, Solace	Land of Havilah Parasite Formula, Infection Formula, X-Ceptic Formula	HerBiotic Extract or Herb Mix, GI Soother, Infection Formula (not for camelid/equine), Super Garlic Immune Formula, Better Bowels, Better Daze Herb Mix, Moringa Powder, Vitalerbs	Herbal Worm Formula
Parasites—Mange, Mites	Dyna Shield, Herbal Tonic, SOD	See Lice	Wounderful! Salve, long-term Fresh Start or DWorm A, HerBiotic Salve, Complete Tissue & Bone Formula	Herbal Worm Formula
Parasites—Meningeal, Flukes, Lungworm	Herbal Tonic, Excel, Miracle Clay, SOD, Trace Minerals Concentrate	Land of Havilah Parasite Formula	DWorm MLL Tincture, DWorm A, Lung Support Tincture, Breathe Tea, Fresh Start, Blood & Cell Support Herb Mix, HerBiotic, Super Garlic Immune Formula, Infection Formula (not for camelid/equine)	Herbal Worm Formula

Challenge	Dynamite	Land of Havilah Herbals	Fir Meadow LLC	Molly's Herbals
Parasites— Stomach, Pinworms	Herbal Tonic, Excel, Miracle Clay, SOD	Land of Havilah Parasite Formula	DWorm A, DWorm MLL, Better Daze Herb Mix, Vitalerbs, Better Bowels, Garlic Clove(s)	Herbal Worm Formula
Parasites— Tapeworm	Herbal Tonic, Excel, Miracle Clay, SOD	Land of Havilah Parasite Formula	DWorm MLL, DWorm A, Better Daze Herb Mix, Vitalerbs, Better Bowels, Garlic Clove(s)	Herbal Worm Formula
Pinkeye	Solace (topical and oral), Trace Minerals Concentrate (oral)	Herbal Eyebright Formula (extract and capsules)	Eye See Herb Mix, Eye See Salve, Herbal Eyebright Formula, HerBiotic, Better Daze Herb Mix, Moringa Powder, Vitalerbs, God's Greens, Super Garlic Immune Formula	
Pneumonia	Solace, Trace Minerals Concentrate, Ester-C, Hiscorbadyne, SOD	Super Garlic Immune Extract, X-Ceptic Extract, MPR Spray, Sen-Sei Ointment, Lung & Bronchial Formula	HerBiotic Herb Mix or Extract, Lung Support Tincture, Breathe Tea, DCongest Salve on lung areas, Kat's Turbo Onion Poultice, Fir Meadow Cayenne, DCongest Salve, Sen Sei Ointment, Super Garlic Immune Extract	Immune ST
Poison and Toxins— Fern	Miracle Clay, Izmine (topdressed)	Blood Stream Formula, Memory Plus Formula, Nerve Formula Extract, Lobelia Extract	DTox Herb Mix or DVenom Tincture, Better Brain Blend Herb Mix, Heart Support Tincture, Moringa Powder, GI Soother Herb Mix, Blood & Cell Support Herb Mix, Cellebration Cell Support Herb Mix, Fir Meadow Cayenne Powder or Tincture, Memory Plus Formula, Mind-Trac Formula, Blood Circulation Formula, Blood Stream Formula, DWorm A Herb Mix, Better Daze Herb Mix, Vitalerbs	

Poison and Toxins— General	Miracle Clay, Excel, Izmine (topdressed)	Blood Stream Formula	DTox Herb Mix, Dvenom Tincture, Blood & Cell Support Herb Mix, Cellebration Cell Support Herb Mix, Blood Stream Formula, Blood Circulation Formula, Fresh Start Herb Mix, Cayenne Tincture or Powder, DWorm A Herb Mix, GI Soother Herb Mix, Heart Support Tincture, Super Garlic Immune Formula, Lobelia Extract	
Poison and Toxins— Mold	Miracle Clay, Izmine (topdressed), Excel	Liver and Gallbladder Formula, Spirulina extract	Fresh Start Herb Mix, DWorm A Herb Mix, GI Soother Herb Mix, Moringa Powder, Better Daze Herb Mix, Vitalerbs	
Poison and Toxins— Rhododen-dron	Miracle Clay, Izmine (topdressed)	Blood Stream Formula, Lobelia Tincture, Activated Charcoal, Soothing Digestion, Hawthorn Berry Heart Syrup, Blood Circulation Formula	DTox Herb Mix or DVenom Tincture, Heart Support Tincture, GI Soother Herb Mix, Blood & Cell Support Herb Mix, Cellebration Cell Support Herb Mix, DWorm A Herb Mix, Lobelia Tincture, Fir Meadow Cayenne Powder or Tincture, Blood Circulation Formula, Blood Stream Formula, Moringa Powder	
Prolapse	Breeder Pac	Vitalerbs, Herbal Calcium Formula, Infection Formula, X–Ceptic Formula	Bal-Nce Herb Mix, Wheat Germ Capsules, ReBuilld Herb Mix, Wounderful! Salve, HerBiotic Herb Mix, Udder Blast Infusion, Better Daze Herb Mix, Fir Meadow Organic Kelp, HerBamine Tincture, MMune Herb Mix, Fir Meadow Cayenne, Super Garlic Immune Formula, Herbal Calicum Formula, Infection Formula (not for camelids/equine), Vitalerbs, Moringa Powder, God's Greens.	Immune ST

Challenge	Dynamite	Land of Havilah Herbals	Fir Meadow LLC	Molly's Herbals
Puncture Wounds	Tea Tree Oil (flush), Solace (flush)	Stings & Bites Ointment, X-Ceptic Extract	HerBiotic Salve, Wounderful! Salve, Better Daze, Vitalerbs, Moringa Powder	Molly's Marvelous Salve
Rabies	Solace, Trace Minerals Concentrate	Infection Formula (not for equine/camelids), X-Ceptic Tincture, Fresh Garlic, Nerve Formula Extract, Relax-eze Extract, Memory Plus Extract	HerBiotic Herb Mix or Extract, Better Brain Blend Herb Mix, Mel-O Herb Mix, Super Garlic Immune Formula, Infection Formula (not for camelid/equine), Relax-Eze Extract, MindTrac, Memory Plus, Better Daze Herb Mix, Vitalerbs, Moringa Powder	Immune ST
Reproduction Issues	Easy Boy, Breeder Pac, Herbal Green, Yucca	Female Reproductive Formula or Male Reproductive Formula, Hormonal Changease, and Wheat Germ Oil	CyclEaze Herb Mix, Bal-Nce Herb Mix, Hormonal Changease, Male or Female Reproductive Formulas, Wheat Germ Oil, Better Bowels, Lower Bowel Formula, Fresh Start, Blood & Cell Support Herb Mix, Cellebration Cell Support Herb Mix, Blood Stream Formula, Red Raspberry Leaf, Moringa Powder, Better Daze Herb Mix, Vitalerbs, HerBiotic, Super Garlic Immune Formula, MMune Herb Mix	Booster Tonic
Ringworm	Tea Tree Oil	X-Ceptic Formula, Complete Tissue & Bone Formula	HerBiotic Salve, Super Garlic Immune Formula, Better Daze, Moringa Powder, Vitalerbs, Complete Tissue & Bone Formula, Mmune Herb Mix, Fresh Start Herb Mix, Fir Meadow Essential Oils: Tea Tree, Lavender	Immune ST, Molly's Marvelous Salve

Condition				
Seizures	Easy Boy, Izmine, DMG	Nerve Formula, Relax-Eze Formula, Complete Tissue & Bone Formula, Anti-Spasmodic Extract or Lobelia Tincture/Extract	Fir Meadow Cayenne, Lobelia Extract, Better Brain Blend, Mel-O Herb Mix, Better Daze Herb Mix, Vitalerbs, Moringa Powder, NerveEaze Salve, ReBuild Herb Mix, Fir Meadow Organic Kelp, Wounderful! Salve, Complete Tissue & Bone Formula, Relax-Eze Formula, Ear & Nerve Extract, Anti-Spasmodic Extract	Ow-Eze
Selenium Deficiency and Toxicity	Toxicity: MSM; Deficiency: Premium E-Selenium	Vitalerbs, Pumpkin Seed for deficiency, Liver and Gallbladder for both.	Kop-Sel Herb Mix for either; also Fresh Start Herb Mix, Better Daze Herb Mix, Vitalerbs	
Sore Mouth/Orf Virus	Trace Minerals Concentrate, Solace, Super Stress, SOD, Ester-C, Hiscorbadyne	Infection Formula (not for equine/camelids), X-Ceptic Tincture, Vitalerbs	HerBiotic Herb Mix or Extract and HerBiotic Salve on the sores, MMune Herb Mix, Super Garlic Immune Extract, Oil of Oregano, Infection Formula (not for camelids/equine), Better Daze Herb Mix, Vitalerbs, Moringa Powder, Wounderful! Salve	Ow-Eze
Stress	Relax (oral), Tranquil (oral), Easy Boy, Dyna Pro	Nerve Formula, Relax-Eze Formula	Better Daze Herb Mix, Vitalerbs, Relax-Eze, Mel-O Herb Mix, Moringa Powder, God's Greens	Aches N' Painz Salve
Structure Misalignment	Release (topical)	Complete Tissue & Bone Formula (ointment/massage oil & powder/capsule), Vitalerbs	Wounderful! Salve, Rebuilld Salve, Complete Tissue & Bone Formula, ReBuilld Herb Mix, HerBamine Tincture, Better Daze Herb Mix, Vitalerbs, Moringa Powder	Molly's Marvelous Salve, Immune ST

Challenge	Dynamite	Land of Havilah Herbals	Fir Meadow LLC	Molly's Herbals
Tetanus	Super Stress, Trace Minerals Concentrate, Solace	Infection Formula (not for equine/camelids), X-Ceptic Tincture, Anti-Spasmodic or Lobelia Tincture or Extract	HerBiotic Herb Mix/Extract, Super Garlic Immune Formula, Infection Formula (not for camelid/equine), Garlic Clove(s), Lobelia Extract, MMune Herb Mix, Better Daze Herb Mix, Vitalerbs, Moringa Powder, Oil of Oregano, Fir Meadow Organic Kelp, NervEaze Salve, Anti-Spasmodic Tincture.	Immune ST
Toxemia	Dyna Spark, Excel, Miracle Clay, Izmine, Solace, Trace Minerals Concentrate	Infection Formula (not for equine/camelids), X-Ceptic Tincture, Fresh Garlic, Blood Stream Formula	ClostridEaze Herb Mix, Better Daze Herb Mix, Vitalerbs, Fir Meadow Cayenne, Blood & Cell Support Herb Mix, Cellebration Cell Support, Blood Stream Formula, DTox Herb Mix, DVenom Tincture, Fresh Start Herb Mix, Garlic Clove(s), Super Garlic Immune Formula, Infection Formula (not for camelid/equine)	
Ulcers	Miracle Clay, Trace Minerals Concentrate	Soothing Digestion Formula	GI Soother Herb Mix, Fir Meadow Cayenne, Better Daze Herb Mix, Vitalerbs, Moringa Powder	Slippery Elm Bark
Urinary Tract Stones	DynaPro, Herbal Green, Catalyst Water	Kidney Formula	Kidney, Bladder & Stones Tincture or Herb Mix, Better Daze Herb Mix, Vitalerbs	E Z P

Condition				
Venom, Stings	Wound Salve, Miracle Clay, Hiscorbadyne, Ester-C, Balm, DynaPro	Plantain Poultice, Liver/Gallbladder Formula Extract, Bites & Stings Ointment, Echinacea Tincture	DBug Salve, DVenom Tincture, DTox Herb Mix, Wounderful! Salve, Fresh Start Herb Mix, Echinacea Tincture, Kid-E-Well Extract, Kid-E-Mune Extract, Better Daze Herb Mix, Moringa Powder, Vitalerbs	Molly's Marvelous Salve
Viral Infections	Trace Minerals Concentrate, Solace, Super Stress, SOD, Ester-C, Hiscorbadyne	Infection Formula (not for equine/camelids), X-Ceptic, Fresh Olive Leaf Tincture, cleanse for body system involved	HerBiotic Herb Mix or Extract or Salve, MMune Herb Mix, Super Garlic Immune Formula, Oil of Oregano, Infection Formula (not for camelid/equine), Better Daze Herb Mix, Moringa Powder, Vitalerbs; also products for the specific body system or organ affected	Immune ST

Resources

Books

The Accessible Pet, Equine and Livestock Herbal: Choosing Abundant Wellness for Your Creatures
Katherine Drovdahl, MH CR CA DipHIR CEIT

Goats: Homeopathic Remedies
George Macleod

Natural Goat Care
Pat Coleby

Natural Remedies for Goat Diseases
Mark Gilberd

Articles

"Goat Pastures *Sericea lespedeza*," *eXtension*, July 2, 2014, www.extension.org/pages/19420/goat-pastures-sericea -lespedeza. An excellent article on the effectiveness of lespedeza as goat forage and in internal parasite management.

C. Edgar Sheaffer, "Natural Approaches to Parasite Control," February 2011, www.clarkvetclinic.com/ images/natural_approaches_to_parasite_control.doc. A thorough article on parasite control written by a well-known veterinarian homeopath.

Websites

Albion Knowledge Base
Detailed information about chelates, chelation, and the manufacturing process compiled by Albion Minerals. www.albionnutritionalfacts.com/index.php/knowledge -base/about-knowledge-base

American Holistic Veterinary Medical Association

The AHVMA offers a search function for locating a holistic veterinarian near you. The site allows you to search by animal specialization and treatment modalities.
www.ahvma.org/find-a-holistic-veterinarian

EFT Tapping Therapy

The official EFT Tapping website with instructions and tutorials by EFT founder Gary Craig.
www.emofree.com

FDA Pet Food Labels—General

FDA information about pet food labeling regulations.
www.fda.gov/AnimalVeterinary/ResourcesforYou
/ucm047113.htm

Tellington Touch

The official website for TTouch training, with information on training sessions and how to locate a practitioner.
www.tellingtontouch.com

Fias Co Farm

The online site of Fias Co Farm, run by Molly Nolte of Molly's Herbals, is basically an entire book about goat health and husbandry presented as web pages with easy-to-navigate links.
www.fiascofarm.com

Shopping

Boiron

Founded in France in 1932, today Boiron is one the leading suppliers of homeopathic products in the United States.
www.boironusa.com
1-800-BOIRON-1

Dr. Bach's Original Flower Remedies

Where to purchase and learn about Dr. Edward Bach's thirty-eight remedies, developed in the 1920s in England.
www.bachflower.com

Dynamite Specialty Products

If you are already using Dynamite, contact your current Dynamite distributor. If you would like to purchase Dynamite products from me, please use the second link.
www.dynamitespecialty.com
www.dynamitemarketing.com/carrieeastman

Fir Meadow LLC

The website and online shop of Kat Drovdahl, master herbalist and vitalist. There are many essential oil practitioners out there, but Kat is a good resource for goat essential oil use. Fir Meadow also offers herb mixes, supplements, and bulk herbs.
www.firmeadowllc.com

Land of Havilah

Land of Havilah Herbals offers herbal mixes, bulk single herbs, and essential oils, among other things. All orders include personal guidance from master herbalist and shop owner Kristie.
www.landofhavilahfarm.com
kristie@landofhavilahfarm.com

Molly's Herbals

Molly's Herbals has provided herbs, supplements, and custom herbal formulas for the holistic care of animals since 2004.
www.mollysherbals.com
molly@mollysherbals.com

Native American Nutritionals

There are many essential oil companies out there, but this is my current personal favorite.
www.nativeamericannutritionals.com

Redmond Natural

The official website for Redmond Natural trace mineral sea salt. Although you can't buy directly from this site, you can use it to find local suppliers.
www.redmondnatural.com

Rocky Mountain Oils

Another great site for essential oils.
www.rockymountainoils.com

Wachters Organic Sea Products

Since 1932, Wachters has been crafting an array of sea vegetation nutritional products for everything from human and animal care to soil and plant conditioner.
www.wachters.com

Waiora

Waiora, a healthy living company founded in 2004, is a good source for zeolite drops.
www.mywaiora.com/482339

Washington Homeopathic Products

Originally founded in 1873 as the Washington Homeopathic Pharmacy, WHP is the oldest-full-line homeopathic pharmacy in the United States.
www.homeopathyworks.com
1-800-336-1695

Additional Information

To contact the author please visit www.carrieeastman.com or www.oakhillfaintinggoats.com. E-mail energeticgoat@carrieeastman.com

Index

nosodes, 66
nutritional labels, 72, 75, 77–78
nux vomica, 66

oats, 58, 59
one-hand finger test, 21–23

parasites, 15, 37, 58, 63, 64, 65, 82–84
pasture, xiii, 47, 65, 71, 84
permission, 8, 53–54
pesticides, 63
polarity
    clearing, 4–5
    definition of, 2
    flipped, 3–4, 70–71
potassium, 5, 74–75
prebiotics, 58, 65, 80, 81–82, 84
probiotics, 58, 80, 81, 84
protein, 58, 59, 68, 79
    copper and, 71, 73
push-pull test, 23–25

qi. *See* chi
qion, 33

rapeseed. *See* canola
ration balancing, 60–61, 70–71
ration calculator, 60, 63
Rees, M. L., 33
reflex points
    chart, 41
    clearing, 36
    direct versus surrogate, 35, 36
    point priorities, 36, 43
    principles of, 2, 33–34, 36
    using in diagnosis, 34–36, 37–38, 40

remedies, 8, 30–31, 38–40, 42–43
    herbal, 84
    samples, 11–12, 37
    testing for, 29–31, 40, 42

salt, 5, 74–77
selenium, 34, 41
sodium. *See* salt
soil health, 59, 60, 69
soy, 58, 60
sulfur, 71, 78
supplements, 5, 48, 59, 60, 63, 64, 65, 68, 69, 71, 74, 85

Tellington TTouch, 13
temporomandibular joint (TMJ), 75–76
testing kits, 11–12, 54, 55
transition to holistic care
    feed, 58–63
    risks of, 8, 57
    steps to, 58–66

vaccines, 63, 64–66
vaccinosis, 66
vibrations, 1, 12, 33, 36, 66
vitamins, 34, 41, 43, 60, 64, 65, 78, 85

weight, 5, 37, 47, 58, 60, 63, 83

zeolites, 63, 65, 66, 84
zinc, 41, 65, 71

About the Author

Carrie Eastman was drawn to animals and healing at a very young age, when a family friend shared her knowledge of Reiki, Touch for Health, and nutrition. From the time she could toddle, Carrie thought all kids got muscle tested, supplemented, and taken to the chiropractor for injuries. She carried crystals home in her lunch box, spent hours in the woods, helped her dad garden, and had a variety of pets, from dogs and cats to fish, guinea pigs, rabbits, and snakes. As a teenager, Carrie handled Si-

berian huskies in conformation and junior showmanship classes. She started riding horses during elementary school, learning hunt seat and training-level dressage at Connecticut's New Canaan Mounted Troop and Ox Ridge Hunt Club. In high school she drifted away from her Eastern medicine roots and embraced the more conventional Western medicine approaches to animal health, while staying Eastern herself. Losing her horse Buck to a horrible colic nudged Eastman back toward the Eastern medicine path for her animals.

Carrie graduated from Penn State in 1990 with an honors B.S. in wildlife science and additional focused coursework in horse production and crop and soil sciences. In the early 1990s her horse Poco was diagnosed with navicular disease, ringbone, and arthritis at the age of twelve, and he was put out to pasture. In desperation she turned to homeopathy and nutrition, and two years later Poco was again sound. Poco then gave Carrie a wonderful case of whiplash, which led her to a chiropractor who practiced bio energy work, which in turn led her to Dr. Regan Golob. Dr. Golob developed the Bio-Energy Analysis Technique, which combines acupressure, craniosacral therapies, chiropractic, reflex points, applied kinesiology, Bio Energetic Synchronization Technique, defense physiology, and other modalities into a powerful system that frees the body to heal itself. Carrie apprenticed under Golob and became a student of TTEAM and TTouch, also getting her Level I Centered Riding certification.

Around that time Carrie was working on improving her pastures and decided to get a couple goats to balance the vegetation. She fell head over heels for their fun personalities, as well as the balance they brought to her land. As a fan of rare breed conservation, she decided to get involved with breeding myotonic goats, commonly called fainting goats. She began adapting the methods she had learned to her goats. Today Carrie continues to study health and healing, soils, crops and nutrition, as well as conscious horsemanship and balanced hoof trimming. In her spare time, she helps to keep the farm repaired, improves her building techniques, gardens, and tinkers with old machines. She shares her home with three horses, a herd of myotonic goats, chickens, dogs, cats, fish, turtles, and of course her wonderful family.

Also from Acres U.S.A.

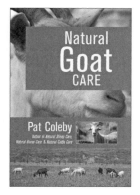

Natural Goat Care
Pat Coleby

Goats thrive on fully organic natural care. As natural browsers, they have higher mineral requirements than other domestic animals, so diet is a critical element to maintaining optimal livestock health. In *Natural Goat Care*, consultant Pat Coleby shows how to solve health problems both with natural herbs and medicines and the ultimate cure, bringing the soil into healthy balance. Topics include: correct housing and farming methods; choosing the right livestock; diagnosing health problems; nutritional requirements and feeding practices; vitamins and herbal, homeopathic and natural remedies; psychological needs of goats; breeds & breeding techniques. ISBN *978-0-911311-66-2, Softcover, 371 pages.*

Alternative Treatments for Ruminant Animals
Paul Dettloff, D.V.M.

Drawing on 36 years of veterinary practice, Dr. Paul Dettloff presents a natural, sustainable approach to ruminant health. Copiously illustrated chapters "break down" the animal into its interrelated biological systems: digestive, reproductive, respiratory, circulatory, musculoskeletal and more. Also includes a chapter on nosodes, with vaccination programs for dairy cattle, sheep and goats. An information-packed manual from a renowned vet and educator. ISBN *978-1-601730-12-1, Softcover, 260 pages.*

Paramagnetism
Philip S. Callahan, Ph.D.

This book is the culmination of all of Callahan's previous works and will certainly be his most popular book to date and a classic for years to come. In this one, beautiful little book, Callahan lays out a lifetime of research into low-frequency forces in nature and his discoveries regarding the force of paramagnetism and the amazing effects it has upon soils, plants and people. Join Phil Callahan as schooling, research, life experiences, insight and inspiration come together for the benefit of humankind. Amply illustrated by the author. ISBN *978-0-911311-49-5, Softcover, 128 pages.*

To order call 1-800-355-5313
or order online at www.acresusa.com

Natural Cattle Care

Pat Coleby

Natural Cattle Care encompasses every facet of farm management, from the mineral components of the soils cattle graze over to issues of fencing, shelter and feed regimens. *Natural Cattle Care* is a comprehensive analysis of farming techniques that keep the health of the animal in mind. Pat Coleby brings a wealth of animal husbandry experience to bear in this analysis of many serious problems of contemporary farming practices, focusing in particular on how poor soils lead to mineral-deficient plants and ailing farm animals. Coleby provides system-level solutions and specific remedies for optimizing cattle health and productivity. ISBN *978-0-911311-68-6, Softcover, 198 pages.*

A Holistic Vet's Prescription for a Healthy Herd

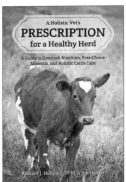

Richard J. "Doc" Holliday, D.V.M. & Jim Helfter

Learn to heal your cattle by treating the cause and not the symptoms. Holistic veterinarian Richard "Doc" Holliday is here to share the secrets he's learned from more than fifty years of experience in animal nutrition and health. Holliday reveals how animals are capable of self-regulating their trace mineral needs when provided with a free-choice selection of minerals. Inside this book you'll find studies on animal nutrition as well as a veterinarian's real-life experiences with nutritionally wise livestock. In addition, Doc takes on some of his most frequently asked questions regarding animal health to provide the reader with a clear idea of some organic and holistic solutions to common cattle care issues such as mastitis, milk fever, and calving. Anyone can prove the fundamental concepts of animal health by watching and learning from animals, who will share their secrets with us if we are attentive. ISBN *978-1-601730-88-6, Softcover, 156 pages.*

Grass, the Forgiveness of Nature

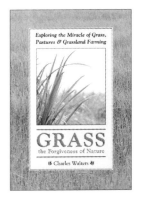

Charles Walters

What is the most important plant in the world? In terms of nutritive content, function within the ecosystem, and even medicinal properties, the answer to this question may very well be grass. In this wide-ranging survey of grass forages and pastureland, Charles Walters makes the case that grass is not just for cows and horses — that in fact it is the most nutritious food produced by nature, as well as the ultimate soil conditioner. You will learn from traditional graziers who draw on centuries of wisdom to create beautiful, lush, sustainable pastures, as well as cutting-edge innovators who are using such methods as biodynamics and sea-solids fertilization to create some of the healthiest grasslands in the world. ISBN *978-0-911311-89-1, Softcover, 320 pages.*

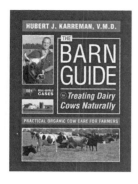

The Barn Guide to Treating Dairy Cows Naturally

Hubert J. Karreman, V.M.D.

A hands-on barn and field guide designed for quick and easy use, presenting a thorough examination of animals in the barn and then listing symptoms with many pictures of what the farmer is seeing, possible conclusions, and then giving a concise set of treatments. The treatments are ones that Dr. Karreman has found to work consistently well during 15 years in the trenches working with organic cows. Basic backgrounding in the fundamentals for organic and holistic thinking about livestock is included in the introduction. The companion guide to *Treating Dairy Cows Naturally*, this book includes an easy-to-follow visual and hands-on physical exam section, features nearly 100 case studies organized by symptoms, and offers valuable field-tested natural treatments. ISBN *978-1-601730-23-7, Softcover, 191 pages.*

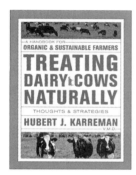

Treating Dairy Cows Naturally

Hubert J. Karreman, V.M.D.

Drawing upon veterinary treatments from the days before synthetic pharmaceuticals, and tempering them with modern knowledge and clinical experience, Dr. Karreman bridges the world of natural treatments with life in the barn in a rational and easy to understand way. In describing treatments for common dairy cow diseases, he covers practical aspects of biologics, botanical medicines, homeopathic remedies, acupuncture and conventional medicine. By incorporating conservation principles, he also alerts us to the need of keeping our waterways clean — both for our health and the health of the cows. This book should serve as a useful reference for years to come. *ISBN 978-1-601730-00-8, Hardcover, 412 pages.*

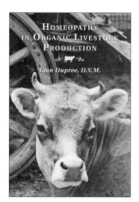

Homeopathy in Organic Livestock Production

Glen Dupree, D.V.M.

Going beyond homeopathic theory and philosophy, *Homeopathy in Organic Livestock Production* contains an extensive discussion of the most common maladies that will help readers recognize symptom complexes and take logical steps so you can move from patient to remedy, regardless of the species, ailment or the type of farm involved. *ISBN 978-1-601730-16-9, Softcover, 176 pages.*

To order call 1-800-355-5313
or order online at www.acresusa.com

Acres U.S.A. — our bookstore is just the beginning!

Farmers and gardeners around the world are learning to grow bountiful crops profitably — without risking their own health and destroying the fertility of the soil. *Acres U.S.A.* can show you how. If you want to be on the cutting edge of organic and sustainable growing technologies, techniques, markets, news, analysis and trends, look to *Acres U.S.A.* For over 40 years, we've been the independent voice for eco-agriculture. Each monthly issue is packed with practical, hands-on information you can put to work on your farm, bringing solutions to your most pressing problems. Get the advice consultants charge thousands for . . .

- Fertility management
- Non-chemical weed & insect control
- Specialty crops & marketing
- Grazing, composting & natural veterinary care
- Soil's link to human & animal health

To subscribe, visit us online at

www.acresusa.com

or call toll-free in the U.S. and Canada

1-800-355-5313

Outside U.S. & Canada call 512-892-4400

fax 512-892-4448 • info@acresusa.com